THE BICENTENNIAL COLLECTION OF AMERICAN MUSIC

Volume I - 1698-1800

Compiled by
Elwyn A. Wienandt

Book layout and design by Jim Tyckoson

Published by HOPE PUBLISHING COMPANY
Carol Stream, Illinois 60187

TABLE OF
CONTENTS

A WORD FROM THE PUBLISHERS

As we enter our 82nd year, the Hope Publishing Company is proud to make available this carefully edited compilation of historic American music. All of the works in this volume were composed, performed and published during our formative years as a Republic. Although the Bicentennial of 1976 was a motivating factor in this effort, we feel that there will be a continuing importance to the projection of our national heritage through the music that so aptly reflects these early years of our country.

We were particularly pleased when Dr. Elwyn A. Wienandt, Associate Dean of the Academic and Instrumental Division of the Baylor University School of Music, Waco, Texas, and an acknowledged authority in the field, agreed to undertake this important project. Utilizing the resources of the Baylor University library micro-card reprints, as well as the Frances G. Spencer Collection of Early American Music (over 21,000 pieces), Dr. Wienandt has recreated the fabric of the times in this delightfully readable history for both formal and informal study. It is also an excellent source for music making in the home, which along with the church, served as a primary performance area during our country's first 100 years.

Hope Publishing Company

PREFACE

Music that survives from the eighteenth century shows that two types of Americans were being served by composers, teachers, and purveyors of the art. For the most part, the country was inhabited by people who had no training in reading music and who had no strong interest in learning much about the process. Understanding the notation of the simple melodies that served as the musical basis for hymns was quite enough, and any learning beyond that represented a sophistication that served choral rather than congregational singing. A small part of the population retained a taste for the art music of their former homelands. These people were responsible for the continuation of interest and skill in instrumental music and in some choral music with instrumental accompaniment. The salons of the emerging upper class had a place for keyboard music, a repertory of songs such as were fashionable in England, and a limited amount of music for other instruments, such as flute, violin, guitar, or clarinet.

In centers where money, leisure time, and taste came together—such places as Boston, New York, Baltimore, Philadelphia, Charleston, and Williamsburg—there were subscription and benefit concerts before the end of the eighteenth century, as well as stage entertainments provided by musicians and actors who had immigrated from England and the Continent. But these events were no more characteristic of the general musical taste than is concert activity in our own time. The collection of pieces in this first volume is intended to show the broadest possible musical activity, from village artisan to urban statesman. It contains, therefore, music for religious gatherings and private devotions, music that well-bred young ladies could perform by voice or at the keyboard for gatherings of friends, and music that brought a taste of foreign culture to the new land. The influences of patriotism, longing for the world abroad, religious music that followed the traditions of one sect or another, or simply music designed for teaching the growing public how to perform better, all ran together in what flowed from the presses.

Many notable Americans touched upon music either as amateurs or in connection with their callings. Thomas Jefferson and Patrick Henry were acceptable violinists, Francis Hopkinson performed and composed, George Washington sought out performances for his listening pleasure, and Benjamin Franklin made significant modifications in the glass harmonica. *Paul Revere*, shown at his silversmith's workbench in Copley's portrait, cast church bells and engraved music for printing. Five years before his well-known "midnight ride" (which did not reach its destination since he was captured by the British), he engraved the plates for William Billings's first collection, *The New-England Psalm-Singer*.
(Courtesy Boston Museum of Fine Arts).

Capitalization, spelling, and punctuation of text material in early American publications tends to be extremely varied. Some volumes capitalize all proper nouns; others avoid capital letters as a rule. A few publications do without punctuation in text that is set to music; others separate phrases with semicolons and colons. Word divisions do not conform to modern usage in many cases. The solution reached here is to deal with spelling, punctuation, and capitalization as it is given unless the meaning is rendered unclear, in which case the modern form is added in brackets. If word divisions occur, they are reproduced as in the original; if there are none, words are divided according to modern use.

Grateful acknowledgement is made to the following: The librarians and staff of Crouch Music Library and Moody Memorial Library of Baylor University; William Lichtenwanger of The Music Division, Library of Congress; Hans Nathan, Michigan State University; Ewald V. Nolte and Karl Kroeger of The Moravian Music Foundation; Julia Z. Keehn, Lititz, Pennsylvania; and the Graduate Research Committee of Baylor University for research funds supplied in connection with parts of this study.

Permission to reproduce musical and pictorial material has been granted by the following: Abbey Aldrich Rockefeller Folk Art Collection; Board of Selectmen, Marblehead, Massachusetts; Chicago Historical Society; Colonial Williamsburg Foundation; Culver Pictures; The John Carter Brown Library, Brown University; The Moravian Historical Society, Nazareth, Pennsylvania; The Moravian Music Foundation; Museum of Fine Arts, Boston; Réunion des Musées Nationaux, Paris; Time/Life Syndication Service; The Union League of Philadelphia; and Yale University Art Gallery.

Much music-making surely went on that we cannot discuss or illustrate intelligently. What is provided here is a cross-section of what was put into print to serve one or another of those groups mentioned above. Most of the music sung by soldiers, farmers, housewives, children, or tradesmen at their occupations or in their relaxed evenings has been lost or has been strained into the common cauldron of folk music, from which it can never be retrieved in its original form. Here, then, is what can be reconstructed from the evidence, in a form that is illustrative rather than comprehensive. We must remember that there can well have been a large amount of music that escaped documentation of any sort. Even the simplest and least sophisticated of what is collected in this volume may be more highly developed than the folk music of a large portion of eighteenth-century America's citizens.

Several peculiarities of eighteenth-century music and text have been modified for the convenience of the reader. Choral music of that period, for example, often reversed the position of tenor and soprano from what we expect to find. The parts have been restored to the positions used in modern editions. Some music was written in basically white-note values, the half-note being the unit of pulse. Such pieces have been changed to our common usage with the quarter-note carrying the pulse. Instructions about tempo and dynamics appeared with irregularity in such music and, only when necessary, additions have been made here. Such additions are enclosed in square brackets for convenient identification.

Cambridge Short Tune S.M.

Bay Psalm Book
9th edition, 1698

Psalm 70

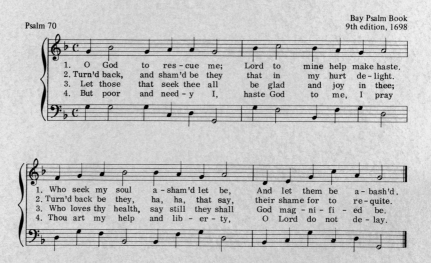

1. O God   to res-cue me;   Lord to   mine help make haste.
2. Turn'd back,   and sham'd be they   that in   my hurt de-light.
3. Let those   that seek thee all   be glad   and joy in thee;
4. But poor   and need-y I,   haste God   to me, I pray

1. Who seek my soul   a-sham'd let be,   And let them be   a-bash'd.
2. Turn'd back be they,   ha, ha, that say,   their shame for to   re-quite.
3. Who loves thy health,   say still they shall   God mag-ni-fi-ed be.
4. Thou art my help   and lib-er-ty,   O Lord do not de-lay.

1698

CAMBRIDGE SHORT TUNE

It is uncertain how the early American settlers amused themselves with music, but we know that the first music printed in North America was intended for the worship of God. The first book of metrical psalms compiled by Americans was the Bay Psalm Book, and it contained no music in its first eight editions. Music from imported psalters, and old melodies that remained in their memory, provided the settlers with enough tunes for a time. The 1698 edition, however, contained thirteen tunes in a variety of meters sufficient to accommodate the rhymed psalms. The tunes were printed in two parts, but it is possible that they were sung in unison more often than not. Certainly no instruments were permitted in those early religious services.

Since most of the poetry was in common meter (8.6.8.6.), nine of the tunes were also in that scheme. *Cambridge Short* (also called *Southwell* in some English collections of that time) is a short-meter tune (6.6.8.6.), and is the only one of its type in the Bay Psalm Book. It is printed here because it is not commonly found in American collections, although a modified version of *Southwell* appears in some modern hymnals. The tunes of the Bay Psalm Book were not written by Americans, but were chosen from existing English sources. It was to be nearly three-quarters of a century before original music by Americans would come into print.

THE PSALMS, HYMNS, AND SPIRITUAL SONGS, OF THE OLD & New Testament . . . (Boston: Printed by B. Green and J. Allen, 1698).

Canterbury Tune C.M.

Psalm 1, verses 1 & 2, N. Brady and N. Tate, *A New Version of the Psalms of David* (London, 1704; reprinted, Boston: J. Allen for Benjamin Elliot, 1720)

T. Walter, *The Grounds and Rules of Musick Explained*, 1721

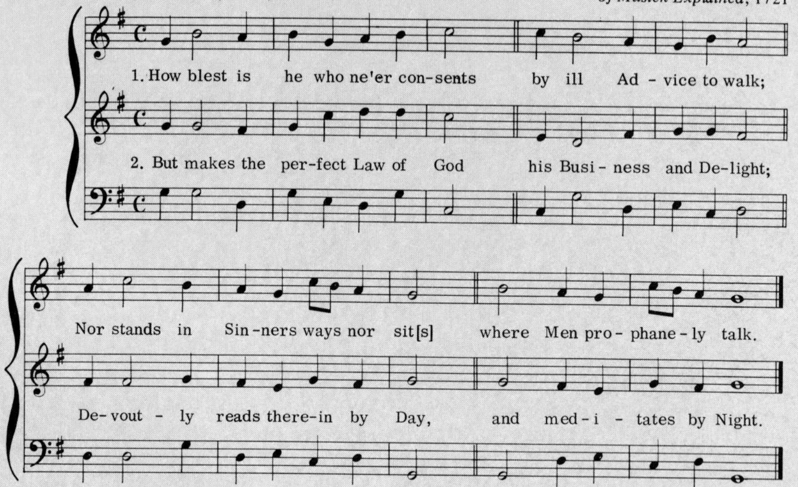
1. How blest is he who ne'er con-sents by ill Ad - vice to walk;
2. But makes the per-fect Law of God his Busi- ness and De-light;
Nor stands in Sin-ners ways nor sit[s] where Men pro- phane - ly talk.
De- vout - ly reads there-in by Day, and med - i - tates by Night.

Psalm 1, verses 1 & 2, N. Brady and N. Tate, *A New Version of the Psalms of David* (London, 1704; reprinted, Boston: J. Allen for Benjamin Elliot, 1720.)

1721

CANTERBURY TUNE

The printing of early American music in two or more parts did not necessarily prove that the music was sung in that manner. The first half of the eighteenth century was a period of furious debate. On the one side were those who sang only the psalm tunes that had been handed down by rote or that were "lined out" by a precentor before each hymn was sung. On the other were the advocates of musical literacy, the proponents of singing by note. Had the former won out, the cause of musical progress in this country would have been set back for untold decades. The strong efforts of the supporters of learning included the publication of volumes that contained both instructional material and a number of tunes that could be sung for religious services or private worship. American ministers were among those who saw the need for musical understanding, and four of them were among the leaders who published supporting treatises and instruction books. Thomas Symmes, John Tufts, Nathaniel Chauncey, and Thomas Walter strongly urged the expansion of the religious repertory, quoting Scripture to support their views just as their opponents took a negative stand appropriately girded by biblical authority.

The year 1721 saw the publication of several volumes that were designed to help the American public learn to sing by note. The first to provide tunes in three parts was Thomas Walter's instructional collection *The Grounds and Rules of Musick Explained.* The music is borrowed from English sources, as was customary at that time. While it is possible that all three parts were sung by the really skilled singers, the upper melody could be sung independently or supported by whatever instruments were at hand.

Thomas Walter, *The Grounds and Rules of Musick Explained: Or an Introduction to the Art of Singing by Note. Fitted to the meanest Capacities.* (Boston: Printed by J. Franklin for S. Gerrish, 1721).

100 Psalm Tune New

Psalm 100, v. 1, from
The Bay Psalm Book

John Tufts,
An Introduction to the Singing of Psalm Tunes (1726)

Shout to Je-ho-vah, all __ the earth. With joy-ful-
ness the Lord serve yee. Be-fore his pres-ence
come with mirth. Know that Je-ho-vah God __ is hee.

4

100 PSALM TUNE NEW

Music notation, as it was used for the simple psalm tunes of the eighteenth century, was not difficult to learn. Still, it was an unusual and foreign tongue to the untutored. It is no wonder that efforts were soon made to reduce the difficulties notation brought to the public. The substitution of alphabet letters for notes was relatively easy, even though the use of only four letters, FSLM, as abbreviations for the solfege syllables they represented, exposed a problem about whether the syllables were to be sung high or low in the scale. The Bay Psalm Book had used notes and letters together. Tufts' *Introduction* used only the letters, but gave the necessary clues as to exact pitch by placing them on a staff. Punctuation marks served to indicate the duration of pitches, and the tunes were probably soon committed to memory since they were short. Substitutes for standard notation have been proposed at regular intervals in history. None of these early American proposals, even though they were sufficient for the needs of the day, gained general acceptance until the use of shaped notes early in the nineteenth century.

The *100 Psalm Tune New* has not been traced to any English source. Irving Lowens, one of the leading scholars of early American music, believes this may be the first piece to be composed and published in North America. A number of books had come into print in Mexico City before the Bay Psalm Book, but they never had an influence on our traditions inasmuch as they were the products of Spanish Catholicism, local in use and foreign to the developments in North America. If this psalm tune is the earliest original piece to come from American Protestantism, it is an isolated example. The first authenticated original composition is printed in 1761, a full thirty-five years later.

Since the Bay Psalm Book was still widely used in the 1720s, it is chosen as the source for the words printed with the tune here.

John Tufts, *Introduction to the Singing of Psalm-Tunes* (5th ed., Boston: S. Gerrish, 1726).

Der XXIII 23. Psalm

Neu-vermehrt und vollständiges Gesang-Buch (1753)

Mein hü - ter und mein hirt ist Gott der Her - re,

Drum fehlt mir nichts von dem, was ich be - geh - re,

Auf ei - ner grü - nen au - en er mich wei - det,

Zum schö - nen fri - schen was - ser er mich lei - tet,

Er - quickt mein seel von sei - nes ne - mens we - gen

Ge - rad er mich führt auf den rech - ten ste - gen.

1753

DER XXIII.
PSALM

So much attention has been devoted to the influence of England in our early musical history that the influence of settlers from other countries is often overlooked. It was not only the well-known Ephrata Cloister and the various settlements of Moravians that made a musical impression through music with German text, but also various congregations of the Reformed Dutch Church. The first Reformed Dutch hymn book with German text was printed in this country in 1752 (*Geistreiche Lieder*...Germantown, Christoph Saur). It contained only a few tunes, although there were many hymn texts as well as the Gospels and Epistles. In the following year an expanded book was issued, and it is from that volume that this melody for the twenty-third Psalm is taken. The phrases are rhythmically identical except for the second, which differs in its second and third notes more probably because of a misprint than by intention.

The printing of an unadorned melody does not indicate any less musical participation or interest on the part of the Reformed community. All branches of Calvinism traditionally avoided harmonized settings. Since no effort was being made to teach parishioners the fundamentals of music or the skills of part singing, there was no need to print more than the tune.

Neu-vermehrt und vollständiges Gesangbuch Worinnen sowohl die Psalmen Davids (Germantown: Christoph Saur, 1753).

Time has been frozen at Colonial Williamsburg where the eighteenth century survives in architecture, costumes, and atmosphere. Raleigh Tavern and its visitors would have looked the same then as they do in this picture. Lighted Christmas trees were not known in this country, nor was the custom of caroling, but the greenery adorning the Tavern clearly heralds the joyous season. *Raleigh Tavern Exterior, Christmas.* (Colonial Williamsburg Photograph).

1761

CHRISTMAS

The first published book containing compositions by native-born Americans was James Lyon's *Urania.* Lyon took compositions from a number of English sources, and he included a number of his own efforts as well as a setting of *The 23rd Psalm* by his friend, Francis Hopkinson. Lyon simply entitles his two-part setting *Christmas.* It is a hymn text by Nahum Tate that has remained current to our day. Although he has been scorned as England's worst poet-laureate, Tate has outlived his critics by his contributions to psalmody as half of the famous team of Tate and Brady, and he is known to many secular musicians as the librettist for Henry Purcell's opera *Dido and Aeneas.*

The music Lyon used here was borrowed in 1787 by John Aitken for *A Compilation of the Litanies and Vespers, Hymns and Anthems as they are Sung in the Catholic Church,* in which the text was changed as follows:

> Whilst Angels to the world Proclaim;
> The Birth of Christ our King;
> To magnify his sacred Name
> we'll joyful Anthems sing.
> The watchful Shepherds seiz'd with Fear
> At radiant Light divine;
> when they the happy tiding hear,
> the [illegible] in their hallelujahs join.

Whether it was Tate's widespread acceptance by Protestants that caused Aitken to use a substitute text is not clear. His new version encountered difficulty in measure 16, however, where the rest in the upper voice causes "shepherds" to be divided without regard for continuity. More of Aitken's strange treatment of material for the Catholic market can be seen beginning on page 74.

James Lyon, *Urania or a choice Collection of Psalm-Tunes, Anthems and Hymns From the most approv'd Authors, with some Entirely New . . .* (Philadelphia, 1761).

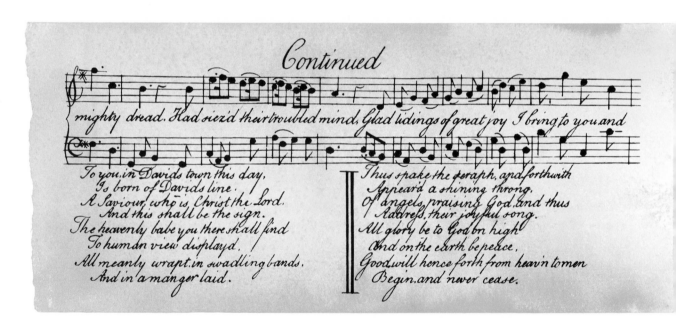

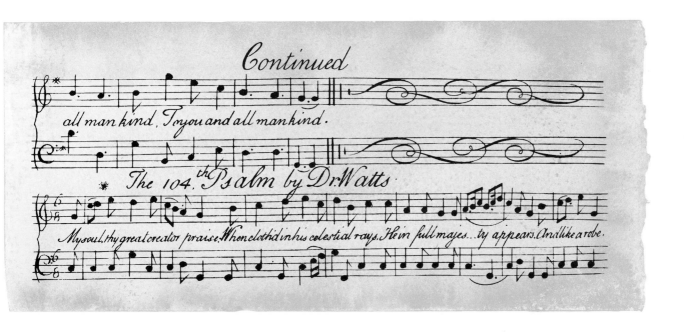

CHRISTMAS
1761

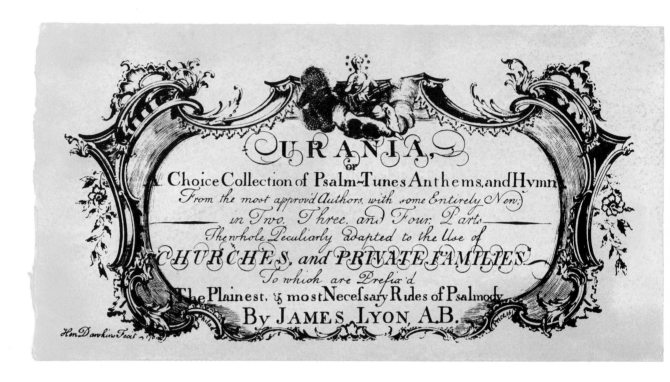

URANIA,
or
A Choice Collection of Psalm-Tunes Anthems, and Hymns
From the most approv'd Authors, with some Entirely New;
—— in Two, Three, and Four, Parts ——
The whole Peculiarly adapted to the Use of
CHURCHES, and PRIVATE FAMILIES
To which are Prefix'd
The Plainest, & most Necessary Rules of Psalmody
By JAMES LYON, A.B.

Hen. Dawkins Fecit

1761

THE THEORETICAL INTRODUCTION FROM URANIA

Anyone who knows how few teachers of music, how few choirs, and how few trained musicians inhabited this new country finds it difficult to conceive a use for the large variety and number of music collections intended for group singing in the church and the home. For the most part, the answer lay in the presence of a theoretical self-instructor in each volume of music, a primer that laid out the elements of notation, musical practice, and, in some cases, taste. Such introductions had been common in the tune books that were imported from England, and they continued to be printed in the publications that were produced here.

Ideally, it should have been possible for a musical illiterate to buy such a book, study the theoretical introduction, and be able to sing his part from the pieces in any collection. Actually, we must assume that a great deal of amateur teaching took place, the more experienced assisting the lesser, thereby making it possible for individuals to gather almost immediately in performance of the psalm-tunes, and later, the set-pieces and anthems printed in the collections.

The *Urania* introduction contained all that one needed to sing along, but certainly not enough for one to sing well. The curious student might

The Gamut, or Scale of Music.

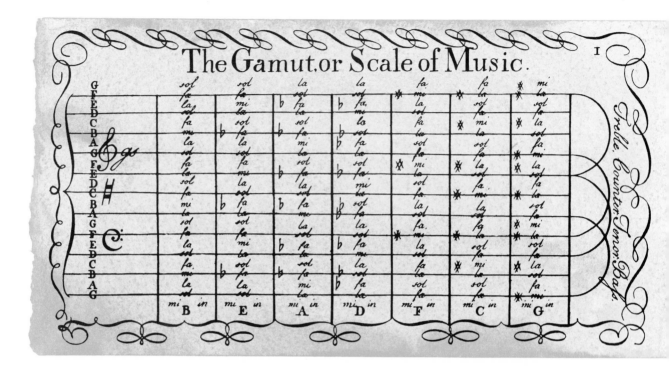

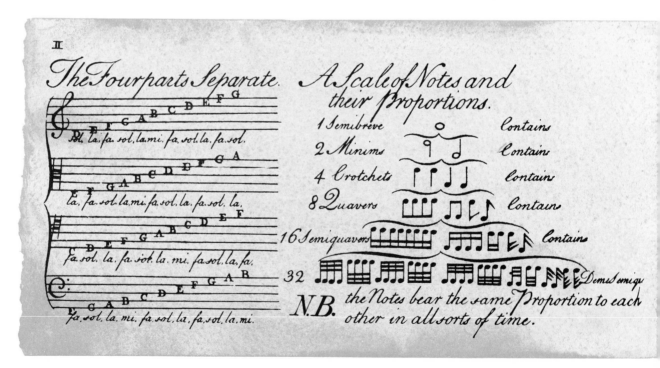

II

The Four parts Separate.

A Scale of Notes and their Proportions.

1 Semibreve — Contains
2 Minims — Contains
4 Crotchets — Contains
8 Quavers — Contains
16 Semiquavers — Contains
32 — Demisemiqu

N.B. the Notes bear the same Proportion to each other in all sorts of time.

14

Explanation of the Gamut.

The 4 Parts of Music. are distinguished from one another. by 4 Semicircles. each including 5 Lines.with their Proper Cliffs and Letters. The first is the Bass, or lowest Part in Music. and known by the F Cliff ⊕ which always stands on F. The 2.ᵈ is the Tenor.with the C. Cliff ‖ on C. its 4.ᵗʰ Line. The 3.ᵈ is Counter with the C Cliff ‖ on C. its 3.ᵈ Line: And the 4.ᵗʰ is Treble, the highest part of Music, with the G Cliff 𝄞 on G. its 2.ᵈ Line. The F & G Cliffs in most Authors are immovable, but when they move. the Letters.which are the Names of the Lines and Spaces, always move with them, in the same order as they stand in the Gamut. The C Cliff is movable in all Authors. but. the Line it stands on is always C, and must be sounded a 5.ᵗʰ above the F Cliff. and a 5.ᵗʰ below the G Cliff. except when the latter is prefix'd to a part design'd for mens Voices.(which is frequently the case. with the Tenor & Counter in this Book) then it is a 4.ᵗʰ above the G Cliff, for that is now an Octave.(or 8 Notes) below its usual place.and Unison (or the same sound) with the highest G in the Bass.

find some unanswered questions along the way. The first page shows the gamut; that is, the entire range of pitches possible to be sung in a group of mixed voices, along with the range for each voice part. The solmization syllables that make up the diagram are incomprehensible to anyone not receiving additional instruction from an experienced musician, one familiar with the four-syllable system that then prevailed. The procedure is quite clear to the modern singer who recognizes that *mi* is the designation for the seventh scale-step.

The directions for singing (page x), are limited to the barest essentials. They do not, by any stretch of the imagination, suffice even for that day. Left unstated is the problem of tone production, and all matters of taste and judgment are similarly avoided. Such things can be considered the responsibility of the singing master, that itinerant teacher who appeared in increasing numbers after the middle of the century. The stay of such a man in any community was limited by the market for his talents.

The four Monosyllables sol. la. mi. fa. seldom change the Order in which they stand in the Gamut: viz. from mi to mi ascending they are fa. sol. la. fa. sol. la. &: descending la. sol. fa. la. sol. fa; And the two Semitones or half Notes in every Octave are invariably fix'd between mi & fa. & la & fa. throughout all the Removes of mi, except when a Flat, Sharp, or Natural, is plac'd immediately before some particular Note. All Notes upon Lines & Spaces, not mark'd with either Flats or Sharps, are call'd Natural Notes, & are represented by the Monosyllables in the 2ᵈ Column of the Gamut. In all the succeeding Columns, they are remov'd to other Letters by Flats & Sharps, according to the following Rules, but in such a manner, that they express those Flats & Sharps, without affecting any of the Natural Notes.

1. When neither a Flat nor Sharp is set at the Beginning of a Tune, **Mi** is in B. But,
2. If B. be flat, **Mi** is in E.
3. If B. & E. be flat, **Mi** is in A.
4. If B. E. & A. be flat, **Mi** is in D.
5. If B. E. A. & D. be flat, **Mi** is in G.
6. If F. be Sharp, **Mi** is in F.
7. If F & C be Sharp, **Mi** is in C.
8. If F. C. & G. be Sharp, **Mi** is in G.
9. If F. C. G. & D. be Sharp, **Mi** is in D.

Of Time, or the Duration of Sounds in Music.

V

Time is of two Kinds, viz. Common, & Triple, in one or the other of which all Movements are included. Common Time is measured by an even Number of Beats in each Bar, the first half of which must be Perform'd with the Hand or Foot down, & the other with it up; Its first Mood is a very slow & grave Mobement, containing one Semibreve, or its Quantity, in every Bar, which ought to be Sounded about 4 Seconds, or while you may leisurely say 1. 2. 3. 4. This Mood is mark'd thus. ☐C The 2ᵈ Mood has a line drawn thro' the C ☐₵ & should be sung about half as fast again as the first. The 3ᵈ Mood is known by a C. inverted ☐Ɔ from which it is called the Retortive Mood, or by a Figure of Two ☐2 And must be sung as quick again as the first Mood. The last Mood worthy of Notice in this Place is Mark'd thus ☐2/4 & called 2 to 4 containing one Minim or two Crotchets &c. in a Bar, which require nearly the same Time that ye same Notes require in the 2ᵈ Mood, In beating the 2 first of these Moods the Hand should have 4 equable Motions in every Bar, 2 down & 2 up. And in the 2. last Mood only 2 Motions, one down and the other up: According to the following Examples in Common Time, where d is put for down, & u for up: and the Number of Beats in each

Bar

16

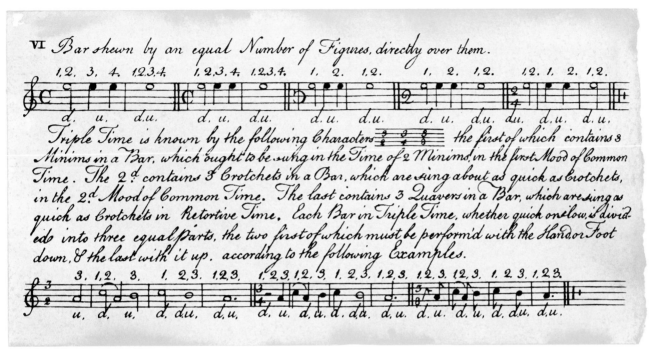

VI *Bar shewn by an equal Number of Figures, directly over them.*

Triple Time is known by the following Characters $\frac{3}{2}$ $\frac{3}{4}$ $\frac{3}{8}$ *the first of which contains 3 Minims in a Bar, which ought to be sung in the Time of 2 Minims in the first Mood of Common Time. The 2.d contains 3 Crotchets in a Bar, which are sung about as quick as crotchets, in the 2.d Mood of Common Time. The last contains 3 Quavers in a Bar, which are sung as quick as Crotchets in Retortive Time. Each Bar in Triple Time, whether quick or slow, is divided into three equal Parts, the two first of which must be perform'd with the Hand or Foot down, & the last with it up. according to the following Examples.*

When the basics had been learned by the residents who were interested in being introduced to musical skills, the singing master usually wound up his activities with a "Singing Lecture." The local pastor would deliver a sermon on the propriety and beauties of psalmody, and there would follow a demonstration of the skills learned by the new singers. Generally, these must have been modest affairs attended only by members of the community. There is a record of a larger gathering, probably not unique, that took place at Neshaminy, Pennsylvania, in 1789. Members of several nearby singing-schools gathered at the Presbyterian Church there for the Singing Lecture. The sermon was given by the Reverend Samuel Blair, and the music was led by a Mr. Spicer who probably had trained the voices in the several communities during the previous weeks. The event is described in a letter of an anonymous female visitor. She seems to be reporting on the event as part of a vacation trip out of the city. The pertinent section of her letter is given verbatim.

Example of Rests.

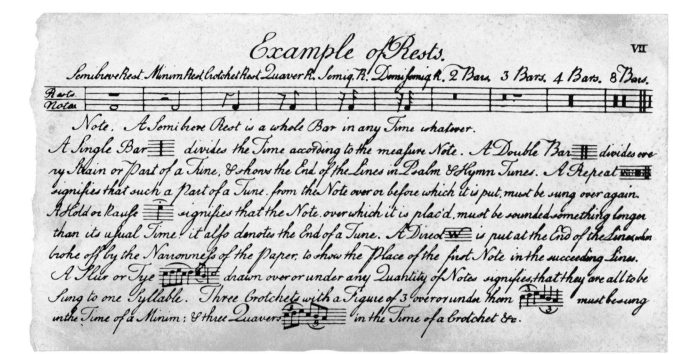

Semibreve Rest. Minim Rest. Crotchet Rest. Quaver R. Semiq. R. Demisemiq R. 2 Bars. 3 Bars. 4 Bars. 8 Bars.

Rests.
Notes.

Note. A Semibreve Rest is a whole Bar in any Time whatever.

A Single Bar ⎯ divides the Time according to the measure Note. A Double Bar ⎯ divides every Strain or Part of a Tune, & shows the End of the Lines in Psalm & Hymn Tunes. A Repeat ⎯ signifies that such a Part of a Tune, from the Note over or before which it is put, must be sung over again. A Hold or Pause ⎯ signifies that the Note, over which it is plac'd, must be sounded something longer than its usual Time; it also denotes the End of a Tune. A Direct ⎯ is put at the End of the Lines, when broke off by the Narrowness of the Paper, to show the Place of the first Note in the succeeding Lines. A Slur or Tye ⎯ drawn over or under any Quantity of Notes signifies, that they are all to be Sung to one Syllable. Three Crotchets with a Figure of 3 over or under them ⎯ must be sung in the Time of a Minim; & three Quavers ⎯ in the Time of a Crotchet &c.

Of Flats Sharps & Naturals.

A Flat ⎯ placed before any Note signifies that, that Note (and all on the same Letter in that Bar, except mark'd to the contrary) must be sung a Semitone lower than its Natural Pitch. The Sharp ⎯ is of a contrary Nature, and raises a Note a Semitone higher than its Natural sound. When Flats are set at the Beginning of a Tune, they affect all the Notes on the same Letters, on which they stand, thro' the whole Movement; thus if a Flat be set on B, B must be sounded half a Note lower than its Natural Pitch, thro' the Tune, unless the Flat is removed by a Sharp or Natural. Sharps set at the Beginning of a Tune have the contrary Effect. A Natural ⎯ reduces any Note, made flat or sharp by the governing Flats or Sharps in the Beginning of a Tune, to its primitive Sound.

Of the Keys in Music.

The Letter, on which a Tune closes, is called its Key, which is known to be either flat or Sharp by the third above the last Note in the Bass: if that third contains two whole Tones, the Tune is on a sharp Key, but if only a Tone & Semitone, it is a flat Key.

18

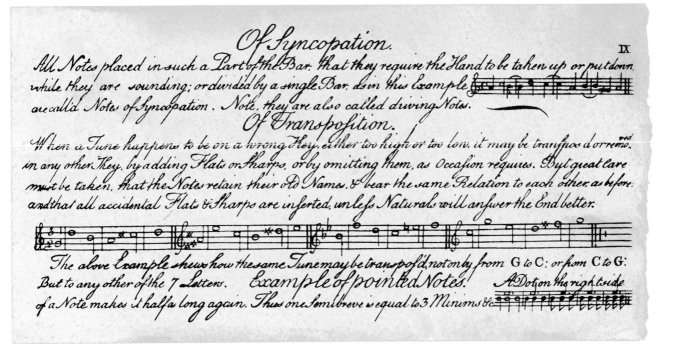

We had about two hundred and fifty singers; who were arranged in the order of the art, on the front floor of the gallery. They were all, I may say, well dressed; that is, in rurul (*sic*) simplicity and elegance. Many of the girls were, really, very handsome. This circumstance, added to the sweetness and harmony of their voices, and the sweeter harmony and innocence of, what may be called, the *toute ensemble* of their appearance, must have inspired you with a very charming sentiment. They all, indeed, seemed to be well taught and practiced in the tunes, and different forms of music, which they sang; and many of their voices were remarkably fine. The several parts of counter, treble, tenor, and bass were so judiciously adjusted and proportioned, and the time was so accurately observed, that not a jar, or any kind of insipidity, or dissonance, offended the ear. A very pleasing order, decency, and, indeed, solemnity, was maintained throughout the performance. One blunder, however, I know not from what cause, was committed. But they recovered from it, at the instance of their

Of the Graces in Music.

Trill. Explaind, Beat. Explaind, Forefall. Expl. Backfall Expl. Turn. Expl. Shake turnd Expl. Grace of Transit

The Trill or Shake is used on all descending prickt Crotchets; on the latter of two Notes on the same Line or Space; and generally before a Close. The other Graces are seldom used in plain Church Tunes but are very proper in Hymns & Anthems. Note, the Turn may be used on a Note, that sinks a semi tone below two Notes on the same Line or Space. always beginning with the first; and also at the end of a Strain, when the last Note is grac'd, as in the following Examples

Some Directions for Singing.

1. In learning the 8 Notes, get the Assistance of some Person, well acquainted with the Tones & Semitones.
2. Chuse that Part, which you can sing with the greatest Ease, and make yourself Master of that first.
3. Sound all high Notes as soft as possible, but low ones hard and full.
4. Pitch your Tune so that the highest and lowest Notes may be sounded distinctly.

The eight Notes Ascending & Descending.

Thirds, ascending and descending.

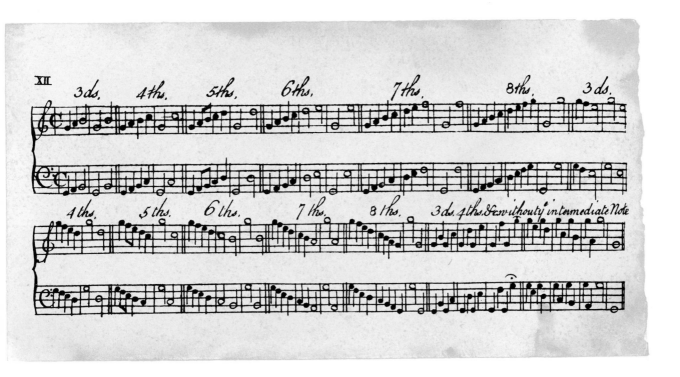

monitor, with so much address, that, in the event, it did them not a little honour. I was not sensible of its having produced the least confusion. The auditors, as I was informed, consisted of between eleven and twelve hundred persons. They were apparently attentive to the preacher, and delighted with the music.

James Lyon, *Urania or a choice Collection of Psalm-Tunes, Anthems and Hymns From the most approv'd Authors, with some Entirely new* . . . (Philadelphia, 1761).

Chorus from
The Military Glory of Great Britain

Largo　　　　　　　　　　　　　　　　　　　　　　　[James Lyon?] (1762)

Pro - pit - ious Powers, who guard_____ our State, let our

Pro - pit - ious Powers, who guard_____ our State, let our

ear - nest Prayer be heard; our Prayer this sol - emn Day pre -

ear - nest Prayer be heard; our Prayer this sol - emn Day pre -

fer'd: Check the Force and Pride_____ of Spain; ren - der all her

fer'd: Check__the Force and Pride_____ of Spain; ren - der all her

22

1762

Chorus from
THE
MILITARY GLORY
OF GREAT
BRITAIN

Public utterances in the years before the general outbreak of hostilities with our parent country often contained strong words of fealty and loyal support of British policy, along with expressions of gratitude for the protection that country's strength afforded us from intrusion by foreign powers. This "Entertainment, given by the late candidates for Bachelor's Degree, at the close of the Anniversary Commencement, held in Nassau-Hall New Jersey September 29th, 1762," is a piece for speakers and chorus. There are six choral sections interspersed by long, flowery speeches about Britain's strength and influence. The various musical sections are entitled:

    I. Britain's Glory
   II. Gallia's Sons shall vaunt no more
  III. Propitious Powers who guard our State
  IV. Glory, Triumph, Victory, Fame
   V. (Most of IV repeated in faster tempo)
  VI. While Mountains poise the balanc'd Globe

The closing chorus is preceded by the spoken phrase, "Long may a GEORGE the regal Sceptre sway." Shortly more than a decade later, the disenchantment with the reigning George led to the rift that made this an independent country.

Ef - forts vain; But Power_ and Glo - ry be_____ Bri-

Ef - forts vain; But Power_ and Glo - ry be_____ Bri-

[Bri-

tan - - - - - -

tan - - - - - -

tan] - - - - - -nia's

[tan] - - - - - nia's

[tan] - - - - - nia's

Fate. Bri - tan - - - nia's

Fate But Power_ and Glo - ry_ be_____ Bri - tan - nia's Fate.

Fate But Power_ and Glo - ry be_____ Bri - tan - nia's Fate.

Fate.

24

Several writers credit the music to James Lyon. If he composed this as well as part of the music in *Urania,* the combination serves to illustrate that he was a man of no mean abilities. His vocal compositions in the religious collection showed him as a competent man with the vocal idiom; the instrumental "symphonies" that appear with some of the choruses indicate that he was acquainted with the prevailing European styles in secular music also. Aside from Lyon's possible connection with this "entertainment," it is interesting as the first secular music printed in the American colonies.

The Military Glory of Great Britain, an Entertainment . . . (Philadelphia: William Bradford, 1762).

A HYMN for Christmas

While sheph^d watch^d their Flocks by night All seated on y^e Gound Y^e Angel of y^e L^d came down, & Glory

Glu----

& Glo-ry

Glo-ry Glo----ry shone around & Glory Glory &c.

Gl----ry Glo----ry shone a roun---d & Glo----ry Glo----ry shone around

----ry Gl'----ry shone around & Glo----ry &c;

Gl----ry Glo----ry shone aroun----d & Glo----ry &

1774

A HYMN FOR CHRISTMAS

Nahum Tate's poem that had been used by James Lyon in *Urania* found another setting in the next decade. John Stickney, who compiled what was the largest collection of religious pieces yet to appear in America, included the version shown here in facsimile. The volume contained 140 psalm and hymn tunes and 30 anthems. It can be seen here how the treble part was written next to the bass, a practice that survived from the past when keyboard performers found accompaniment easier when the principal parts could be seen together. For modern performance the tenors must sing the top staff while sopranos sing the third, and the altos must either sing from alto clef or transpose their part down a seventh.

A question that is rarely asked is "What did the singers do about the later stanzas of a piece like this?" Tune-books of the eighteenth and nineteenth centuries generally provided only the first stanza of these poems. That the complete texts were available in other places did not necessarily make them easily accessible to all who wanted to sing the new tunes. It is probable that they were sung as short, complete settings just as we find them in these volumes, especially in view of the florid closing phrases that are not equally suitable to all stanzas.

John Stickney, *The Gentleman and Lady's Musical Companion* (Newbury-Port: Daniel Bayley, 1774).

America

Isaac Watts

William Billings
(*The Singing Master's Assistant*, 1778)

1774

AMERICA

Composers of psalm and hymn tunes in eighteenth-century American collections were rarely identified, a practice that has led to confusion in a number of cases. Some volumes named composers in the index; others provided no names at all. John Stickney and many other compilers "borrowed" from the volumes of their competitors without scruple, and *America* by William Billings exemplifies the practice. Lifted from *The New-England Psalm-Singer* (1770), it was printed in Stickney's collection without text or composer's name. It was customary to print tunes without words in these volumes, for singers were then free to supply any text of the appropriate poetic meter.

When Billings reprinted the piece in *The Singing-Master's Assistant* (1778), he supplied a text with it and altered the musical content slightly in melodic movement and rhythmic activity. Since he was an ardent nationalist, it might be expected that *America* would have text that reflected his attitudes. That text, printed here with the musical version lifted by Stickney, shows no such direction. While the American flavor of titles sometimes carried into the content of the piece (see page 40) *America* seems to be no more evidence of a rising nationalist spirit than the tune *Breslau* is of Germanic ideas.

John Stickney, *The Gentleman and Lady's Musical Companion* (Newbury-Port: Daniel Bayley, 1774).

thee lift_ up_ mine_ eye.   Up to the hills where Christ is

thee lift up mine eye.   Up to the hills where Christ is

thee lift up mine eye.   Up to the hills where Christ is

thee lift up mine eye.   Up to the hills where Christ is

gone, to plead for all his Saints, pre - sent-ing_ at his_

gone, to plead for_ all his Saints, pre - sent-ing at his_

gone, to plead_for_ all his Saints, pre - sent-ing_ at his_

gone, to plead for_ all his Saints, pre - sent-ing at his_

3 Shillings a Day. 2 Shillings a Day. 1 Shilling a Day.   SIX-PENCE A DAY.   Yankees.   Fire and Water.   Sword and Famine.

This Sketch displays the Hardship a Soldier and his Family endure on the bare Subsistance of Sixpence a Day, while the lowest Trades earn sufficient to enjoy the Comfort of Life.

Published 26 Oct.r 1775 by W.m Humphrey, Gerrard Street Soho.

British troops had been stationed in America for years before the Revolution erupted, at great hardship to the families of soldiers. This 1775 engraving by William Humphrey, published in London, contrasts the plight of those families with the better lot of British tradesmen. (Courtesy Chicago Historical Society)

Anti-war feeling ran high in England, and those opposed to its advocates used various means to air their views. The Political Cartoon for the Year 1775, showing George III being pulled into a chasm by Obstinacy and Pride, appeared in *Westminster Magazine* that year. (Courtesy The John Carter Brown Library, Brown University).

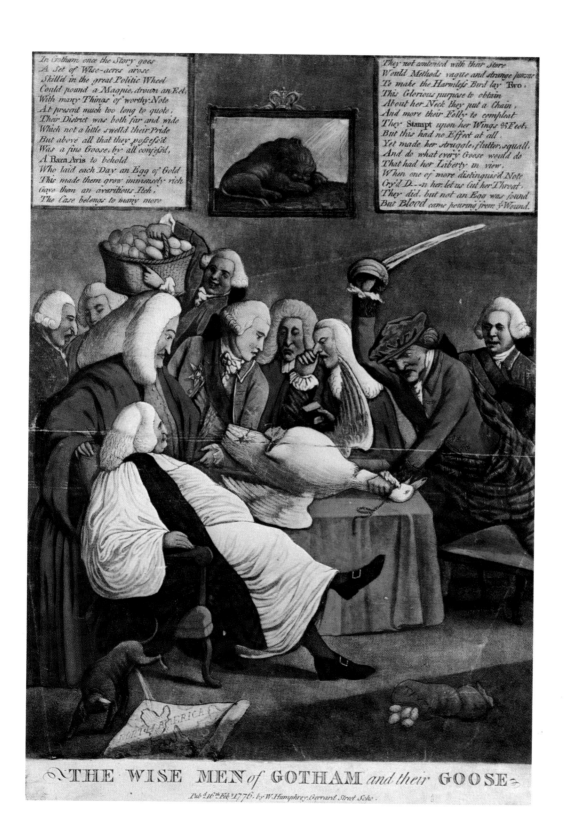

THE WISE MEN of GOTHAM and their GOOSE

Pub.d 16th Feb.y 1776. by W. Humphrey. Gerrard Street Soho.

34

In Gotham once the Story goes
A Set of Wise-acres arose
Skill'd in the great Politic Wheel
Could pound a Magpie, drown an Eel,
With many Things of worthy Note
At present much too long to quote,
Their District was both far and wide
Which not a little swell'd their Pride
But above all that they possess'd
Was a fine Goose, by all confess'd,
A Rara Avis to behold
Who laid each Day an Egg of Gold
This made them grow immensely rich
Gave them an avaritious Itch.

The Case belongs to many more
They not contented with their Store
Would Methods vague and strange pursue
To make the Harmless Bird lay *Two*,
This Glorious purpose to obtain
About her Neck they put a Chain,
And more their Folly to compleat
They *Stampt* upon her Wings & Feet,
But this had no Effect at all,
Yet made her struggle, flutter, squall,
And do what every Goose would do
That had her Liberty in view,
When one of more distinguis'd Note
Cry'd D--n her, let us Cut her Throat,
They did, but not an Egg was found
But *Blood* came pouring from ye Wound.

Feelings over the causes and effects of the war ran so high in England that lampoons of high public figures, including George III, were circulated. William Humphrey, publishing his famous pictorial parody of *The Wise Men of Gotham and their Goose* in 1776, included references to the Stamp Act and Liberty in the printed text. (Courtesy The John Carter Brown Library, Brown University).

Phoebus

From *The Singing Master's Assistant*, (1778)

William Billings

Come let us sing unto the Lord, And praise his name with one ac - cord. In

36

1778

PHOEBUS

A great misunderstanding exists about William Billings's knowledge, skill, and purpose in writing certain of his pieces. Too much attention has been given his comment, "I don't think myself confin'd to any Rules of composition, laid down by any that went before me." He had strong convictions about how his music was to be contrived, and he was equally firm in his ideas about its proper performance. Already in his first book, *The New-England Psalm-Singer* (1770), he showed himself to be a skilled and imaginative composer. Since he had to make his mark in a strongly competitive field, he included the usual didactic introduction for the sake of those who were unfamiliar with music. In his second collection, *The Singing-Master's Assistant,* he stated that the elementary material was omitted because he assumed his readers were familiar with the basic skills.

Phoebus is not characteristic of most of Billings's music. It is a quiet, folk-like piece that would probably gain wide acceptance if the rhythmic thrust did not stall at several points. Performers will find that shortening the note values in a few places (e.g. measures 5, 8, 13, and 18), the piece has an appeal that suits the modern ear without destroying its character.

William Billings, *The Singing-Master's Assistant, or Key to Practical Music* (Boston: Draper & Folsom, 1778).

this___ de - sign___ our cho - rus___ raise. From

this___ de - sign___ our cho - rus raise. From

this___ de - sign___ our cho - rus___ raise. From

this___ de - sign___ our cho - rus raise. From

East to___ West his Praise___ pro - claim. From

East___ to West his Praise pro - claim. From

East___ to West___ his Praise___ pro - claim. From

East___ to West___ his Praise___ pro - claim. From

Pole___ to Pole___ ex - tol___ his_ Fame. The

Pole___ to Pole___ ex - tol___ his Fame. The

Pole___ to Pole___ ex - tol___ his Fame. The

Pole___ to Pole___ ex - tol___ his Fame. The

skies___ shall ech - o back___ his Praise.

skies___ shall ech - o back___ his Praise.

skies shall ech - o back___ his Praise.

skies___ shall ech - o back___ his Praise.

39

Lamentation Over Boston

Paraphrase of Psalm 137

William Billings
(*The Singing Master's Assistant*, 1778)

1778

LAMENTATION OVER BOSTON

The impact that was made upon American music publishing by the Revolutionary War is apparent in comments made by William Billings in his second book, *The Singing-Master's Assistant*.

By way of Apology, I take this Method to acquaint the Public, that the Book of Anthems which I promised them was just upon the point of publication, when hostilities commenced between Britain and the Colonies; which Unhappy War was the sole motive, that induced me to "hang my harp upon the willows" and suppress the publication; but relying so far upon their Candour, as to suppose myself already forgiven, I here renew my former promise of publishing, as soon as our political affairs have assumed a still brighter aspect.

Billings' adoption of typically American names for the tunes in this volume is apparent in such psalm-tune titles as *Stockbridge, Vermont, North Providence, Columbia,* and *Baltimore,* among others. In the same volume, he included an anthem, the text of which was a parody on Psalm 137. The specific act of violence that motivated Billings to write the piece is unknown, but its coming soon after the Battle of Bunker Hill may be reason to relate it to that famous event.

William Billings, *The Singing-Master's Assistant, or Key to Practical Music* (Boston: Draper & Folsom, 1778)

When we re-mem-ber'd thee___ O Bos - ton when

When we re-mem-ber'd thee___ O Bos - ton when

When we re-mem-ber'd thee___ O Bos - ton when

When we re-mem-ber'd thee___ O Bos - ton when

we re-mem-ber'd thee_ O Bos - ton

we re-mem-ber'd thee O Bos - ton As for our friends

we re-mem-ber'd thee_ O Bos - ton

we re-mem-ber'd thee O Bos - ton As for our friends

42

fend them de - liv - er' and re - store them un - to us___

fend them de - liv - er and re - store them un - to us

fend them de - liv - er and re - store them un - to us

fend them de - liv - er and re - store them un - to us

a - gain.___

a - gain.___

a - gain.___

a - gain.___   For they___ that___ hold___ them in

Bond - age re - quired_ of_ them to take_ up Arms_ a -

For - bid it Lord God for -

For - bid it Lord God for -

For - bid it Lord God for -

gainst their Breth - ren. For - bid it Lord God for -

thirst_ for A - mer - i - can Blood. A voice was heard in

thirst_ for A - mer - i - can Blood. A voice was heard in

thirst_ for_ A - mer - i - can Blood. A voice was heard in

thirst_ for A - mer - i - can Blood. A voice was heard in

Rox - bu - ry which ec-cho'd thro' the Con - ti - nent

Rox - bu - ry which ec-cho'd thro' the Con - ti - nent

Rox - bu - ry which ec-cho'd thro' the_ Con - ti - nent weep -

Rox - bu - ry which ec-cho'd thro' the Con - ti - nent weep -

cause of their Dan - ger weep - ing for

weep - ing for Bos - ton weep - ing weep - ing for

weep - ing for Bos - ton weep - ing for

Bos - ton be - cause_ of their Dan - ger. Is Bos-ton my dear

Bos - ton be - cause of their Dan - ger. Is Bos-ton my_dear

Bos - ton be - cause_ of their Dan - ger. Is Bos-ton my_dear_

Bos - ton be - cause of their Dan - ger. Is Bos-ton my dear_

thee   Then let my num - bers cease to flow Then

thee   Then let my num - bers cease to flow Then

thee   Then let my num - bers cease to flow Then

thee   Then let my num - bers cease to flow Then

be my Muse un - kind   Then let my Tongue for -

be my Muse un - kind   Then let my Tongue for -

be my Muse un - kind   Then let my Tongue for -

be my Muse un - kind   Then let my Tongue for -

get to move_____ and ev - er be con - fin'd.

get to move_____ and ev - er be con - fin'd.

get to move_____ and ev - er be con - fin'd.

get to move_____ and ev - er be con - fin'd.

Let hor - rid Jar - gon split the Air and drive my nerves a -

Let hor - rid Jar - gon split the_ Air and drive my nerves a -

Let hor - rid Jar - gon split the Air_ and_ drive_my_nerves_a -

Let hor - rid Jar - gon split the Air and drive my nerves a -

sun - der. Let hate - ful dis - cord greet my ear as

sun - der. Let hate - ful dis - cord greet my ear as

sun - der. Let hate - ful dis - cord greet my ear as

sun - der. Let hate - ful dis - cord greet my ear as

ter - ri - ble as Thun - der, Let har - mo - ny be

ter - ri - ble as Thun - der, Let har - mo - ny be

ter - ri - ble as Thun - der, Let har - mo - ny be

ter - ri - ble as Thun - der, Let har - mo - ny be

54

ban-ish'd hence and Con-so-nance de - part, Let

ban-ish'd hence and Con-so-nance de - part, Let

ban-ish'd hence and Con-so-nance de - part, Let

ban-ish'd hence and Con-so-nance de - part, Let

dis - so-nance e - rect her throne and reign with-in my Heart.

dis - so-nance e - rect her throne and reign with-in my Heart.

dis - so-nance e - rect her throne and reign with-in my Heart.

dis - so-nance e - rect her throne and reign with-in my Heart.

The Bird

Words by T. & B.

William Billings,
The Psalm-Singer's Amusement (1781)

1781

THE BIRD

The fuging-tune was popular in England some years before it was introduced to this country, and it was introduced by composers who were active before Billings produced any music. *The Bird* is a typical fuging-tune. It has an opening section in which the voices sing consistently together, followed by a section in which the parts enter one after the other. The second part is usually repeated.

It was the overlapping of text that caused the fuging-tune to be criticized by ministers. They felt that any clear communication of the text was lost in such imitative passages, brief though they might be. In *The Singing-Master's Assistant,* Billings gave some practical hints for clear projection of text.

> In fuging Music you must be very distinct and emphatic, not only in the Tune, but in the pronunciation; for if there happens to be a Number of greater Voices in the concert than your own they will swallow you up; therefore in such a case I would recommend to you the resolution (tho' not the impudence) of a discarded Actor who after he had been twice hissed off the Stage, mounted again and with great Assurance he thundered on these words "I will be heard."

The text of *The Bird* is by Tate and Brady. Billings' national pride was tempered by practical good sense, for he often went to the English sources for his texts.

William Billings, *The Psalm-Singer's Amusement* (Boston: Printed by the Author, 1781).

like _____ a tim - rous Bird _____ to

like a tim - rous Bird _____ to

like _____ a tim - rous Bird _____ to

like a tim - rous Bird _____ to

dis – tant moun - tains_ fly Why

dis – tant moun - tains fly

dis – tant moun - tains fly

dis – tant_ moun - tains fly Why should_ I

58

59

dis - - - - tant

should I like a tim-rous Bird to dis-tant moun-tains fly____

dis - - - tant moun - tains to__

dis - tant moun - tains dis - tant moun - tains to

mount - tains moun - tains____ fly

to dis - tant moun - tains fly

dis - tant moun - tains fly

dis - tant moun - tains to dis-tant moun - tains fly

1781

THE WORLD TURNED UPSIDE DOWN

There is a much-repeated story that the British bands at the Surrender of Yorktown played a tune called "The World Turned Upside Down" while the British troops went through the formalities of the surrender. The story can be traced to a report in Alexander Garden's *Anecdotes of the American Revolution* (1828), where the circumstances were already related as third hand information. The marvel of it is that the tale should have been accepted several times since then and that it was, even after it was found impossible to trace a tune of that name, brought to life again in Lewis Winstock's *Songs & Music of the Redcoats* (1970), *The American Heritage Book of the Revolution* (1971), and S. E. Morison's *Oxford History of the American People* (1965). Fortunately, the story is viewed with suspicion in the first of those three volumes; unfortunately, that volume is probably the least known by the general public. Richard S. Hill proved the entire story to be a fabrication in an unpublished study completed about 1961.

In a number of instances the fable has been examined from the standpoint of whether such a piece of music ever existed, or whether it was instead a piece called "Derry Down," or "When the King enjoys his own again," or perhaps might have been a theater piece by Thomas D'Urfey. What should be considered in any case is what such a band might have been like. Certainly the spectacle of row upon row of trumpets, trombones, clarinets, tubas, drums, and the other instruments of the modern band must be put out of the imagination. There is no evidence that the British forces included much in musical personnel except the functional drummers and unspecified melody instruments. The notice given by Garden in his *Anecdotes* says "the British army marched out with colours cased, and drums beating a British or a German march. The march they chose was—*"The world turned up side down."* We know the title of the tune belongs to no music of that date, although the words are found in a number of places such as poems and plays. Most revealing is the fact that the drums beat out a march, and no reference is made to other instruments. The earliest source of this story mentioned drums, the imagination of later writers developed this into a band, then a group of bands, and the tale grew in histories and fiction works.

There is no music. It was a pretty story, but it is perhaps best thought of in connection with Van Blarenberghe's painting, where the fiction is handled with finesse and cannot be altered through repetition.

Louis XVI commissioned Henri Désiré Van Blarenberghe (1734-1812) to paint twenty-four works showing famous battles, among them the American scene "Prise de York-Town." The painting displays a pageantry and countryside that never existed except in his own imagination, for the painter had no first hand knowledge of the situation he was ordered to depict. (Musée de Versailles).

Rondo III

William Brown (1787)

1787

RONDO III

The rapidly developing practice of singing God's praises in congregational and choral groups, and a strong suspicion that instrumental music was ungodly, made America's musical thrust primarily vocal except in urban circles or among the wealthy landowners. Instrumental performance required also the means to provide an instrument, the taste for abstract pieces without text, leisure time for practice, and the sophistication that viewed music making as a private matter as well as a social one. It is not surprising, then, to find that foreign-born composers produced more of the instrumental literature than did native-born men who had little contact with a life that could support it.

William Brown, who really may have been Wilhelm Braun of Kassel, gave a flute concert in Baltimore in 1784, and he became active in Philadelphia the following year. There he became associated with Alexander Reinagle. That he was on the fringe of the city's important social and political activity is evident from his dedication of these pieces to "the Honourable Francis Hopkinson, Esq." Hopkinson was active as a lawyer, was a signer of the Declaration of Independence, strongly supported church music, and composed religious pieces, songs, and poetry. Brown must have recognized that pianos were still not numerous in this new country, for he cautiously specified that the pieces could be played either on the piano or the more prevalent harpsichord. The careful indication of dynamic levels, the exactly notated melodic ornaments, and the presence of a contrasting section in minor mode all show the composer's thorough grasp of the traditional European musical material of that day.

William Brown, *Three Rondos for the Piano Forte or Harpsichord* (Philadelphia: by the Author, [1787]).

71

Kyrie from The
Holy Mass of the Blessed Trinity

Aitken's *Compilation* (1787)

1787

KYRIE FROM THE HOLY MASS OF THE BLESSED TRINITY

The impact of Catholic music on early American life came almost entirely from Spanish settlements. Missions have survived in parts of Texas, New Mexico, Louisiana, Florida, and California, and their importance is documented in various ways. Only rarely, however, is any attention given to the influx of Catholic settlers in the Eastern states, and musical evidence of their practices is still scant. Since much of their activity was limited by liturgical restrictions, American publication was not much in evidence. The necessary service books could be imported in the small numbers that were needed. Still, in 1787 there appeared a curious volume, published by the same John Aitken who was profiting from numerous volumes intended for Protestant use. It is not strange that his musical miscellany did not reflect Catholic propriety to any great extent.

The *Kyrie* of this Mass is a peculiar combination of chant melodies with a bass line, interspersed by short "symphonies" that reflect an instrumental style lifted from Italian music. The borrowing of non-Catholic material extends also to Aitken's using the Christmas piece that had appeared in *Urania* (see page 9). He printed the piece with the music unchanged, altering only the text in order to accommodate the alien faith.

Chris — te — — — — lei - son

Sy.

Chris — te — — — — lei - son

76

77

The volume is prefaced by a recommendation from four clergymen, presumably Catholic. It is not in the nature of an *imprimatur* that declares the volume to be free of matters foreign to the faith; it is, rather, the usual kind of prefatory praise that many volumes carried, but it is by clergymen rather than musicians. The recommendation reads as follows:

WHEREAS John Aitken, of the City of Philadelphia, hath humbly requested our Approbation of a Work he is now preparing to publish at his own Expence, entitled "A Compilation of the Litanies, Vesper Hymns and Anthems as they are sung in the Catholic Church, adapted to the Voice or Organ:" We desiring to encourage an Undertaking so conducive to the Decency and Solemnity of religious Worship, do hereto set our Name in Testimony of our Approbation.
Philadelphia, Nov. 28, 1787.

Revd. JOHN CARROLL
Revd. ROBERT MOLYNEUX
Revd. FRANCIS BEESTON
Revd. LAWRENCE GRAESSL

John Aitken, *A Compilation of the Litanies and Vespers, Hymns and Anthems as They are Sung in the Catholic Church:* . . . (Philadelphia: Thomas Dobson, 1787).

1787

LOBET DEN HERRN ALLE SEINE HEERSCHAAREN

The dominant cultural force in the Colonies was English, and the traditions of that background fed the developing taste of this new country more strongly than did others. Many of America's musical practices, then, either were outright imitations of English models or unconscious reflections of what native-born musicians hoped would be a truly American art. Because the English models were forthright, direct, and generally uncomplicated, whether religious or secular, the music imported and practiced by the Moravian church was beyond the experience and capacities of the native musician outside the larger cities. Even had Americans been attuned to its expression, it would not have affected their musical development greatly, for the Moravians maintained a self-sufficient community.

From the beginning of the sixteenth century, the Moravians were known to have a strong tradition in hymnody. Early in the eighteenth century, the Society was infused with Lutheran influence through its association with Count Zinzendorf in Germany. The Society flourished there, in England, and in this country. Music played an important role in the life of Moravian communities in Pennsylvania, Ohio, and North Carolina, and imported music, as well as some composed locally, used instruments with solo and choral singing after the manner of Lutheran motets and cantatas. In England, of course, members of the Society became familiar with the verse anthem, the English counterpart to the German cantata and the French grand motet.

Johannes Herbst came from the German line of Moravians, worked for a time in England, and finally settled in this country. In each of these places Herbst began to copy out the music that interested him, and he eventually developed the immense collection that now bears his name.

The *Catalog of the Johannes Herbst Collection*, edited by Marilyn Gombosi (Chapel Hill: The University of North Carolina Press, 1970), identifies over five hundred works in the Collection. Many of the pieces originally were composed and performed abroad, but a few are clearly identifiable as having been composed and first performed in America.

Number 333 in the Collection is one of Herbst's own compositions. It was written for the dedication of a new church building in Lititz, Pennsylvania, on August 13, 1787. Herbst directed the orchestra and choirs at the first performance of this piece, and he also played the organ for the service. A few years later he took up residence at Lititz as pastor to that congregation, and he was made a bishop before he left that appointment. The composition deserves comparison with other music written in this country in the same decade, and it is obviously derived from a more sophisticated tradition than the other pieces in this volume. The use of instruments, the employment of two dissimilar choirs, and the setting of a German text all point to a usage that differs sharply from that stemming from the English tune-book tradition. Permission to use this composition has been given by The Moravian Music Foundation, Winston-Salem, North Carolina.

The Moravian Church, Lititz, Pennsylvania, as it looked in 1787. (Courtesy Julia Z. Keehn).

Brethren's Church, Parsonage and Young Ladies Academy, at Lititz, Pennsylvania in 1787, the year the present church was built.

Lobet den Herrn alle Seine Heerschaaren

Psalm 103:21

Johannes Herbst (1787)

Herrn,   lo - bet den Herrn,   al-le Sei-ne Herr-

Herrn,   lo - bet den Herrn,   al-le Sei-ne Herr-

Herrn,   lo - bet den Herrn,   al-le Sei-ne Herr-

Herrn,   lo - bet den Herrn,   al-le Sei-ne Herr-

lo - bet, lo - bet den Herrn,   lobt den Herrn,

lo - bet, lo - bet den Herrn,   lobt den Herrn,

lo - bet, lo - bet den Herrn,   lobt den Herrn,

lo - bet, lo - bet den Herrn,   lobt den Herrn,

83

85

Die – ner, lo – bet, die ihr Sei – nen Wil – len

Die – ner, lo – bet, die ihr Sei – nen Wil – len

Die – ner, lo – bet, die ihr Sei – nen Wil – len

Die – ner, lo – bet, die ihr Sei – nen Wil – len

bet, lo – bet,

bet, lo – bet,

bet, lo – bet,

bet, lo – bet,

90

lo - bet den Herrn, lo - bet den Herrn.

lo - bet den Herrn, lo - bet den Herrn.

lo - bet den Herrn, lo - bet den Herrn.

lo - bet den Herrn, lo - bet den Herrn.

lo - bet den Herrn, lo - bet den Herrn.

lo - bet den Herrn, lo - bet den Herrn.

lo - bet den Herrn, lo - bet den Herrn.

92

The opening measures of Johannes Herbst's manuscript of *Lobet den Herrn, alle Seine Heerschaaren,* composed for the dedication of the Lititz Moravian Church in 1787. (Courtesy The Moravian Music Foundation).

1788

FEDERAL MARCH

In the 1780s the idea of Federalism, government by a union of states under a central government, emerged strongly in this country. While the terminology and the application of the descriptive adjective to parties and movements became somewhat confused, the word was popularly used in speeches, in printed material, and, as a reflection of the times, in music. The words to a number of songs popular in this era mirror this strong movement, and instrumental music also bore the word as a talisman of timeliness. The music of this period stressed religious convictions, patriotism, and a yearning for European culture. Wealthy, educated Americans were most strongly affected by this yearning for an ancestry most of them never knew, but the religious and patriotic impulse flowed equally through all classes.

Alexander Reinagle, an English musician who came to America in 1786, quickly caught the spirit of the new country. While he produced musical performances that appealed to the sophisticated inhabitants of Philadelphia, New York, and Baltimore, he also composed music that was welcomed by a broad spectrum of society. This march, vibrating the strings of patriotism, was a piece that achieved wide popularity.

We have no information about the participants in the original performance of the *Federal March*, but it is unlikely that the violin, piano, or flute, for which the surviving version was arranged, were involved in the "Grand Procession in Philadelphia, the 4th of July 1788," for which the piece was composed. The sections noted for trumpets may well have been played on those instruments, although fanfare sections were sometimes so marked in keyboard music (see item 24.)

Alexander Reinagle, *Federal March* (Philadelphia: John M'Culloch, 1788).

Federal March

An Ode for the 4th of July 1788.

Oh for a muse of fire! to mount the skies
   And to a list'ning world proclaim—
Behold! behold! an empire rise!
   An Æra new, Time, as he flies,
Hath enter'd in the book of fame.
   On Alleghany's tow'ring head
   Echo shall stand—the tiding spread,
And o'er the lakes, and misty floods around,
An Æra new resound.

   See! where Columbia sits alone,
   And from her star-bespangled throne,
Beholds the gay procession move along,
And hears the trumpet, and the choral song—
   She hears her sons rejoice—
   Looks into future times, and sees
   the num'rous blessings Heav'n decrees
And with her plaudit joins the gen'ral voice.

   "Tis done! tis done! my Sons," she cries,
   "In War are valiant, and in Council wise;
"Wisdom and Valour shall my rights defend,
"And o'er my vast domain those rights extend.
   "Science shall flourish—Genius stretch her wing,
   "In native Strains Columbian Muses sing;
   "Wealth crown the Arts, and Justice clean her scales;
   "Commerce her pond'rous anchor weigh,
     "Wide spread her sails,
   "And in far distant seas her flag display.
"My sons for Freedom fought, nor fought in vain;
"But found a naked goddess was their gain:
"Good government alone, can shew the Maid,
"In robes of social happiness array'd."
   Hail to this festival! all hail the day!
   Columbia's standard on her roof display:
And let the people's Motto ever be.
"United thus, and thus united—Free."

1788

AN ODE

The patriotic fervor of Francis Hopkinson was only one of a number of facets to his complex nature. He was well-educated, well-travelled, sophisticated, artistic, and active in political and religious affairs. A highly respected citizen of Philadelphia, a friend and associate of the leaders of the new nation—he was one of the signers of the Declaration of Independence—he appears to have been an active participant in the nation's affairs after the Revolutionary years as well as during them. His ode in honor of Independence Day so well expresses the national excitement that it is offered as the only non-musical example in this collection.

Francis Hopkinson, *An Ode for the 4th of July 1788*. Broadside.

The Trav'ler Benighted and Lost

Andante

Francis Hopkinson (1788)

[f]

[p]

[P]

1. The Trav-'ler be-night-ed and lost,_____ O'er the
2. The tem-pest howls drear-y a - round,_____ And_____
3. No com-fort the wild woods af - ford,_____ No_____

moun-tain pur-sues his lone way, The_____ stream is all can-dy'd with
rends the tall oak in its flight; Fast_____ falls the cold snow on the
shel - ter the Trav-'ler can see-- Far_____ off are his bed and his

Frost, and the I - ci - cle hangs on the Spray; He
ground, And dark is the gloom of the night. Lone
board And his home,_____ where he wish - es to be. His

1788

THE TRAV'LER BENIGHTED AND LOST

Among the compositions of Francis Hopkinson are seven songs that were engraved for publication in 1788. Before the set was printed, the composer put another poem of his own to music. This was added to the volume even though the title page was not changed. It is that eighth song that is printed here.

Hopkinson dedicated the songs to his good friend, George Washington, writing in part as follows:

I EMBRACE, with heart-felt satisfaction, every opportunity that offers of recognizing the personal Friendship that hath so long subsisted between us. The present Occasion allows me to do this in a manner most flattering to my Vanity; and I have accordingly taken advantage of it, by presenting this Work to your Patronage, and honouring it with your Name.

. . . .

With respect to the little Work, which I now have the honour to present to your notice, I can only say that it is such as a Lover, not a Master, of the Arts can furnish. I am neither a profess'd Poet, nor a profess'd Musician; and yet venture to appear in those characters united; for which, I confess, the censure of Temerity may justly be brought against me.

. . . .

However small the Reputation may be that I shall derive from this Work, I cannot, I believe, be refused the Credit of being the first Native of the United States who has produced a Musical Composition. If this attempt should not be too severely treated, others may be encouraged to venture on a path, yet untrodden in America, and the Arts in succession will take root and flourish amongst us.

Hopkinson's reference to this as the first musical composition in this country points up the different manner in which religious music and concert music were considered. Hopkinson had written several pieces of church music prior to this time—his 23rd Psalm was printed in Lyon's *Urania* in 1761, as well as in later volumes, and some earlier manuscript pieces of his are known—but this seems to have been the first of his attempts to emulate the venerated serious composers from abroad to come into print. Hopkinson had visited in England, and his interest in music took him to performances there. His songs appear to reflect the taste of English composers of that period. The practice of writing only the melody and an instrumental bass was common at that time, perhaps a remnant of the days when figured-bass accompaniments implied the complete harmonic background of a song. The carefully worked out dynamic levels in the introduction and conclusion are marks of the composer's schooling in the art of music.

Francis Hopkinson, *Seven Songs for the Harpsichord or Forte Piano* (Philadelphia: T. Dobson, 1788).

AN ORDINATION ANTHEM.   Taken from sundry Scriptures.

Sing,   O ye heav'ns, And be joyful, O earth, And be joyful, O earth; Break forth into singing,

And be joyful,   O   earth.

For the Lord hath comforted his people,   his   people.

O mountains, Break forth into singing,   O   mountains: For the Lord hath comforted his people. For the Lord hath

1792

ORDINATION
ANTHEM

Oliver Holden may be considered an exaggerated example of the late eighteenth-century American church musician. By profession he was a number of things besides musician; by inclination he turned repeatedly to music. He was, at various times, a marine in the navy, a carpenter, a preacher, a peace justice, and a state representative. He taught music, operated a music store, and composed and compiled music for his several collections. He seems to have been influenced by an English musical pattern that was associated with the Lock Hospital in London, a home for indigent children. The music written for that place was intended for children's voices, and generally appeared as two treble parts with bass. Much of Holden's music also took that shape, as the anthem printed here shows. Holden, however, was not writing for children, and we must assume that the voice distribution he had in mind was probably soprano, tenor, and bass.

Concerning the performance of the pieces in *American Harmony,* he wrote, "the Author wishes that the time in general might be slow, and the strains soft." Although many of the pieces can be performed in that manner, the character of the *Ordination Anthem* belies the tempo instruction, and Holden's own dynamic indications negate his general desire for soft strains.

Oliver Holden, *American Harmony* . . . (Boston: Isaiah Thomas, and Ebenezer T. Andrews, 1792).

Ordination Anthem

From *American Harmony* (Holden) (1792)

Oliver Holden

Break forth ___ in - to sing - ing, O

O ___ Earth, Break forth ___ in - to sing - ing, O

___ Break forth ___ in - to sing - ing, O

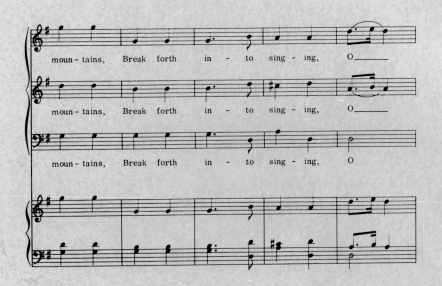

moun - tains, Break forth in - to sing - ing, O ___

moun - tains, Break forth in - to sing - ing, O ___

moun - tains, Break forth in - to sing - ing, O

moun - tains,   For___ the Lord hath

moun - tains, For___ the Lord hath com-fort-ed his peo - ple,

moun - tains,   For___ the Lord hath com - fort -

com-fort-ed his peo - ple, For___ the Lord hath com-fort-ed his

his   peo - ple, For___ the Lord hath com-fort-ed his

ed his   peo - ple, For   the Lord___ hath com-fort-ed his

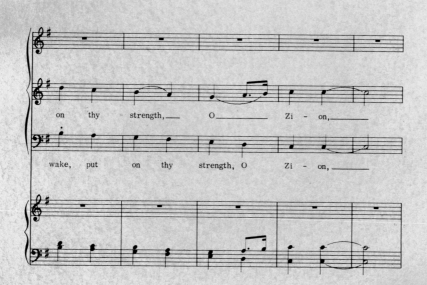

Shake____ thy - self from____ the dust, shake____ thy-

Shake____ thy - self from____ the dust,

self from the dust. A - rise,_____

from the dust. A - rise,_____

And _____ the glo – ry of the Lord, And _____ the

glo – ry of the Lord, And _____ the glo – ry of the

Lord, And _____ the glo – ry of the Lord,

glo – ry of the Lord is ris'n _____ up – on thee.

Lord, is ris'n _____ up – on thee.

And _____ the glo – ry of the Lord is ris'n _____ up – on thee.

How beau-ti-ful up-on the moun-tains are the feet of him that bring-eth good tid-ings, that pub-lish-eth peace.

Hal - le - lu-jah, A - men, a - men,

Hal - le - lu-jah, A - men,

A - men, Hal - le -

a - men, Hal - le - lu-jah, a -

a - men, Hal - le - lu-jah, a - men,

lu - jah, A - men,

D.C. al Fine.

men, Hal-le-lu-jah, Hal-le-lu-jah, a - men.

Hal-le-lu-jah, hal-le-lu-jah, hal-le-lu-jah, a - men.

Hal - le-lu-jah, a - men, a - men.

114

The popularity of stringed keyboard instruments extended to all levels of American society, and the watercolor and ink painting entitled *"To Herr Van Vleck, on His Birthday"* by an unknown artist of 1795 shows an instrument as part of a vocal performance in what appears to be a Moravian household. Regardless of the function of such instruments, their common use demanded that instruction books and pieces such as that which follows be made available.

(Moravian Historical Society, Inc. Nazareth, Pa.)

An Easy and Familiar Lesson

Raynor Taylor (1793?)

1793 ?

AN EASY AND FAMILIAR LESSON

Another of the professional musicians to settle in the New World was Raynor Taylor. His broad musical education in England included training at the Chapel Royal and experience in important church and theater positions. In common with the other foreign-born musicians who worked in this country, he had the skills, the experience, and the standing to write music more varied and interesting than that of the native-born singing-masters who wrote psalm tunes and anthems. Generally, the foreigners produced instrumental music, solo songs, and theatrical works while the native Americans devoted most of their time to religious music.

The movements written by Taylor were pedagogical in nature, and the parts for the two players at a single piano are equal in difficulty. There is no date shown on the printed copy, but it could not have been produced before 1793, the year Benjamin Carr, at whose place of business copies could be purchased, arrived in this country. The rising popularity of the piano is evident in the title, for no mention is made of the formerly ubiquitous harpsichord.

Raynor Taylor, *An Easy and Familiar Lesson for Two Performers on One Piano Forte* (Philadelphia: For the Author, {1793?}).

118

Fandango

Primo

Secundo

Da Capo Gavotta

Da Capo Gavotta

119

Sacred Lines for Thanksgiving Day

Allegro moderato

Hans Gram (1793)

1793

SACRED LINES FOR THANKSGIVING DAY

Each composer who was well versed in the prevailing European musical styles of the 1780s and 1790s attempted to bring something of those styles into his American compositions. Unfamiliarity with the idioms, lack of technical skill among American performers, and the markedly different functions of music on this side of the Atlantic caused otherwise familiar musical ideas to be modified. Hans Gram came to this country from Stockholm about the year 1790, served as a church organist in Boston, infused a number of European ideas into the stream of American thought (including the forceful devices of unison singing as a contrast of harmonic part-singing, the frequent use of the *fermata*, and nonharmonic tones reflective of the elegant, gallant style then popular in Europe).

Gram's contribution of music for a uniquely American religious observance is typical of what many European musicians did when they settled here. They wrote music for days of national significance, regional interest, or for the American churches which they sometimes served as musicians, or, more often, hoped to train through the sale of their religious tune-books. We need to remember that Thanksgiving Day is not a festival borrowed from abroad. Its closest counterpart may be the English Harvest Home Festival, and that cannot be traced earlier than 1843.

This Thanksgiving Day piece is patterned after the English full anthem with verses. It opens with a choral section, has a duo movement, and closes with a choral section. The English prototypes often had three or four times as many sections, but the English church was accustomed to music on a larger scale than was its American counterpart. Since Gram was an organist, we may assume that he provided some kind of support for the duo movement at least. His tempo and dynamics marks are, for the most part, carefully noted, something that American composers usually were not concerned about at this stage. Only the second and third sections of this piece reflect the occasion for which it was composed. The opening chorus is no different from a general anthem, and it could stand by itself as a piece for any religious service.

Hans Gram, *Sacred Lines for Thanksgiving Day, November 7, 1793* (Boston: Isaiah Thomas and Ebenezer T. Andrews, 1793).

sa - cred theme. With joy - ful songs let's praise the Lord, with___

With joy - ful songs let's praise the Lord.

With joy - ful songs let's praise the Lord, with___

sa - cred theme. With joy - ful songs let's praise the Lord.

joy - ful songs,___ let's praise___ the Lord, his bless-ings be our

His bless-ings be our

joy - ful songs,___ let's praise___ the Lord, his bless-ings be our

His bless-ings be our

125

one ac - cord, and mag - ni - fy his name.

one ac - cord, and mag - ni - fy his name.

one ac - cord, and mag - ni - fy his name.

one ac - cord, and mag - ni - fy his name.

Andante

Tenor

Glo - ry to thee_ O gra - cious_ Lord,

Bass

glo - ry to thee,_ O gra - cious Lord, thy boun - ties

fill_ our land, thy boun - ties fill_ our land Thy kind, thy

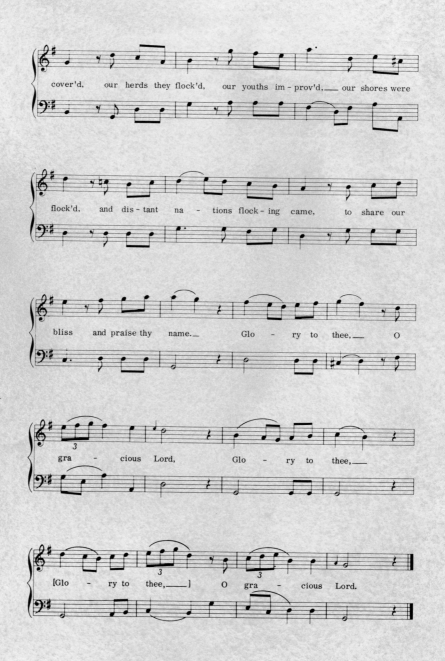

coverd, our herds they flock'd, our youths im-prov'd,___ our shores were flock'd, and dis-tant na-tions flock-ing came, to share our bliss and praise thy name.___ Glo-ry to thee,___ O gra-cious Lord, Glo-ry to thee,___ [Glo-ry to thee,___] O gra-cious Lord.

128

Through all the worlds, ___ through all the worlds, be thou a-

Through all the worlds,

Through all the worlds, ___ through all the worlds, be thou a-

Through all the worlds,

dor'd, through all the worlds be thou a - dor'd, ___ through all the

be thou a - dor'd, ___ through all the

dor'd, through all the worlds be thou a - dor'd, ___ through all the

be thou a - dor'd, ___ through all the

worlds,____ through all the worlds be thou a - dor'd through all the

worlds,_____ be thou a - dor'd,

worlds,____ through all the worlds be thou a - dor'd through all the

worlds,_____ be thou a - dor'd,

worlds be thou a - dor'd through all the worlds be thou a -

be thou a - dor'd,

worlds be thou a - dor'd through all the worlds be thou a -

be thou a - dor'd,

dor'd through all the worlds,____ be thou a - dor'd,____

through all the worlds, be thou a - dor'd,

dor'd through all the worlds,____ be thou a - dor'd,

through all the worlds, be thou a - dor'd,

thou wise,____ thou great, thou boun - teous

thou wise, thou great, thou boun - teous

thou wise,____ thou great, thou boun - teous

thou wise, thou great, thou boun - teous

thou a - dor'd, thou wise, thou_ great, thou boun - teous_

thou a - dor'd, thou wise, thou great, thou boun - teous

thou a - dor'd, thou wise, thou great, thou boun - teous

thou a - dor'd, thou wise, thou great, thou boun - teous

Lord, be thou a - dor'd, through all the worlds, be thou a-

Lord, be thou a - dor'd, through all the worlds,

Lord, be thou a - dor'd, through all the worlds, be thou a-

Lord, be thou a - dor'd, through all the worlds,

dor'd through all the worlds, be thou a-dor'd._____

be thou a-dor'd.

dor'd through all the worlds, be thou a-dor'd._____

be thou a-dor'd.

A - men, a - men, a - men.

A - men, a - men, a - men.

A - men, a - men, a - men.

A - men, a - men, a - men.

134

1793

ANNAPOLIS and PENNSYLVANIA

The popularity of the fuging tune continued unabated through the eighteenth century, and many books served up large portions of the genre. Various degrees of complexity can be found in these pieces, brief though they are. Read's *Annapolis* is a direct expression of text, varied only by the change of meter at the fuging section. The paired notes near the end of the bass part are "choosing notes" which, as Shumway wrote, "stand one over the other, and one only is sung by the same voice." Other compilers indicated that both notes could be sung if enough voices were available.

Shumway's *Pennsylvania* takes its text from Isaac Watts, and the flowing melody is aptly suited to the content, although the composer's lack of technical skill causes a number of spots to lack the strength and level of competence found in the best music of this kind. The device of a "gathering note," a long note at the beginning on which the singers can stabilize pitch, is found as early as the sixteenth century in England. It was quite out of use there by the end of the eighteenth century, but a number of American tune writers employed it. Its presence in American books may be evidence of the limited performing skills of the amateurs who used most of these books, just as the continued printing of instructional prefaces implied the same thing.

Nehemiah Shumway, *The American Harmony* (Philadelphia: John M'Culloch, 1793).

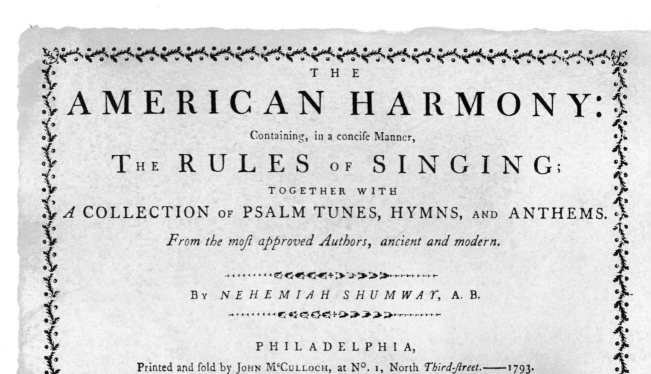

THE
AMERICAN HARMONY:

Containing, in a concise Manner,

THE RULES OF SINGING;

TOGETHER WITH

A COLLECTION OF PSALM TUNES, HYMNS, AND ANTHEMS.

From the most approved Authors, ancient and modern.

BY *NEHEMIAH SHUMWAY*, A. B.

PHILADELPHIA,

Printed and sold by JOHN MᶜCULLOCH, at Nᵒ. 1, North *Third-street.*——1793.

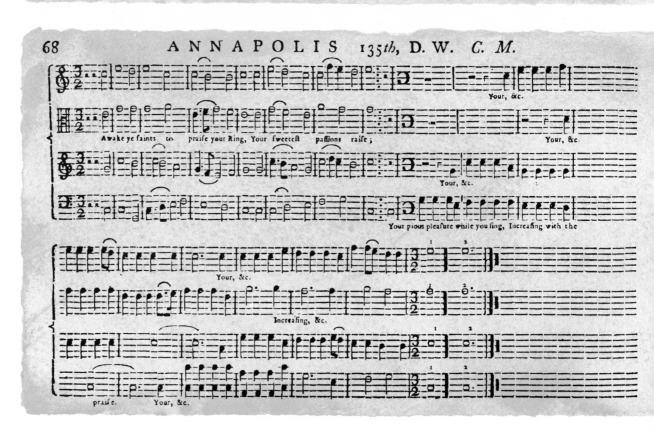

68   ANNAPOLIS 135th, D.W. *C. M.*

Awake ye saints to praise your King, Your sweetest passions raise;   Your, &c.

Your, &c.

Your pious pleasure while you sing, Increasing with the

Your, &c.

Increasing, &c.

praise.   Your, &c.

Pennsylvania

Isaac Watts, *Horae Lyricae*

Nehemiah Shumway,
The American Harmony (1793)

140

THE

Battle of Prague,

a favorite

SONATA,

for the

Piano Forte

COMPOSED BY

F. Kotzwara.

Philadelphia Published and Engraved by JOHN AITKEN, and Sold at his Musical Repository North Second Street, N.º 76 Where may be had Six Sonatas for the Piano Forte composed by Valentine Niccolai, the Philadelphia March composed by R Taylor, Also Aitken's, Collection of Divine Music consisting of Psalms, Hymns, Chants and Anthems for One two three and four Voices.

142

1793

THE BATTLE OF PRAGUE

The composer of *The Battle of Prague* never visited America, and he was already dead two years before his composition was printed here. But the popularity of his piece was to continue for more than half a century everywhere English was the principal tongue. Despite its lack of redeeming musical qualities, it became the most performed, and one of the most widely published pieces in England and America.

What was the great appeal of Franz Kotzwara's only notable composition? If immediacy of expression is a reason for popularity, the piece should have died after no more than a decade, for the memory of that bloody battle in the Seven Years' War was dimmed by the passage of time. It may be that man has always had a need for the depiction of war, even when he abhors it. Medieval troubadours sang of the joy and satisfaction that could be found in serving as a man of arms; battle pieces for voices, lute, or harpsichord were numerous in the Renaissance; military connotations abound in music of the Classical period; Beethoven was convinced that his symphonic *Wellington's Victory* was one of his best compositions; and Tchaikovsky's *1812*

143

Overture has remained popular to our own time.

For the amateur performer or listener, the appeal may have stemmed partly from the ability to understand a long piece of music without text. The listener could comprehend what each section meant; the performer was able, even with limited technical facility, to produce results of seeming significance by playing rapid, but easily mastered patterns, meaningless scale passages, impressive cannon shots while flourishing a cross-hands technique. The instructive captions; signal cannons, bugle calls, flying bullets, galloping horses, cries of the wounded, and the triumphant strains of *God Save the King*, provided a sense of involvement not to be found in a sonata or a complex set of variations. Nor was this desire for pictorial piano music confined to a few pieces. In the

144

nineteenth century one Charles Grobe was to become highly popular as a regular producer of such gems, many of them on subjects traceable in American history. An example of his work will be found in volume two.

After a greater number of touring virtuosi appeared in this country, the taste for keyboard music became broader, if not more elevated. But that time was yet in the future, in the coming century. In the meantime, Kotzwara's *Battle*, printed in this country within four years of its first appearance in England, continued to enthrall performers and listeners alike. The piece was printed in Philadelphia by J. C. Moller in 1793. The facsimile pages printed here are from an edition that appeared early in the next century.

Farewell Anthem-Fragment

From *The American Harmony* (Shumway) (1793)

Jacob French

Soprano: My friends, I am go-ing a long and te-dious jour-ney nev-er to re-turn... Fare you well, fare you well, fare you well, fare you well, fare you well, my friends.

Alto: My friends, I am go-ing a long and te-dious jour-ney nev-er to re-turn... Fare you well, fare you well, fare you well, fare you well, fare you well, my friends.

Tenor: My friends, I am go-ing a long and te-dious jour-ney nev-er to re-turn... Fare you well, fare you well, fare you well, fare you well, fare you well, my friends.

Bass: My friends, I am go-ing a long and te-dious jour-ney, nev-er to re-turn... Fare you well, fare you well, fare you well, fare you well, fare you well, my friends.

1793

FAREWELL ANTHEM, fragment, and THE DYING CHRISTIAN'S LAST FAREWELL 1794

William Billings' advice about the proper way to sing fuging tunes (page 57) was intended to inform his readers about vocal balance and textual clarity. He wrote of other matters as well in his *Singing-Master's Assistant*, even though some of his words seem more pertinent to his *Dying Christian's Last Farewell* of 1794 than to any pieces in his 1778 volume. He said:

I would take this opportunity, to acquaint my younger Pupils, that it is deemed a point of ill manners to invade the province of another, by singing a Solo, which does not belong to your part, for it will admit of these two constructions, viz. that the persons to whom it is assigned,

The Dying Christian's Last Farewell

From *The Continental Harmony* (1794)

William Billings

are not capable of doing justice to the piece, or at least, that you are more capable than they. It is also very degrading to the author to sing, when he (for reasons perhaps unknown to you) by presenting a number of empty Bars tacitly forbids your singing, [since] no doubt this invention of his, is to illustrate some grand point, in the plan of the composition; when, by your ill timed intervention, you not only destroy the sense, intended to be conveyed in the composition; but convey a very different sense to the audience: therefore for you to sing, when the author forbids your singing, is both unmannerly, and ostentatious.

Billings' *Continental Harmony* contained a lugubrious anthem in dialogue. His text was apparently influenced by Alexander Pope's popular "Vital spark of heavenly flame," which had also influenced Jacob French a year earlier. French wrote a traditional musical setting, the opening and closing sections of which are included here. Billings' fertile imagination, however, caused him to give a doleful title to the piece, and to identify the fleeing spirit of the dying Christian with the tenor voice. The tenor, consequently, opens the dialogue and, in a consistency of musical depiction, is kept silent in the closing measures, he having figuratively expired several measures earlier. There is a modern edition of this anthem in which the editor has restored the tenor voice to the final measures, apparently unaware both of Billings' admonition printed in the *Singing-Master's Assistant* and his intention to "illustrate some grand point."

William Billings, *The Continental Harmony* (Boston: Isaiah Thomas and Ebenezer T. Andrews, 1794).

where the wea-ry are at rest. And rest. Where pleas-ures

where the wea-ry are at rest. And rest. Where pleas-ures

where the wea-ry are at rest. And rest. Where pleas-ures

where the wea-ry are at rest. And rest. Where pleas-ures

dwell___ for - ev - er-more, and joys___

dwell for - ev - er-more, and___ joys that nev-er, nev-er___

dwell___ for - ev - er-more, and joys___

dwell___ for - ev - er-more, and___ joys that nev-er, nev-er

151

152

joys that nev - er fade, and joys____ that____ nev - er, nev - er

ev - er-more, and joys that nev - er fade, and joys that nev - er

fade, that nev - er, nev - er fade, that nev - er, nev - er

nev - er, nev - er fade, where pleas-ures dwell for - ev - er-more, and

fade, where pleas-ures dwell for - ev - er-more, and joys that nev - er____

fade, where pleas-ures dwell for - ev - er - more, and joys that

fade, and joys_____ that

joys that nev - er fade,_____ that nev - er, nev - er

fade, ___ that nev-er, nev-er fade, ___ and joys that nev-er

nev-er, nev-er fade, where pleas-ures dwell for ev-er - more, and joys that

nev-er, nev-er fade, that nev-er, nev-er fade, that

fade, that nev-er, nev-er fade, and joys that nev-er

fade, where pleas-ures dwell for ev - er-more, and joys that nev - er

nev-er, nev-er fade, and joys that nev-er fade, where

nev-er, nev-er fade, that nev-er, nev - er fade, and

fade, and joys that nev-er, nev-er, nev-er fade, where pleas-ures

154

155

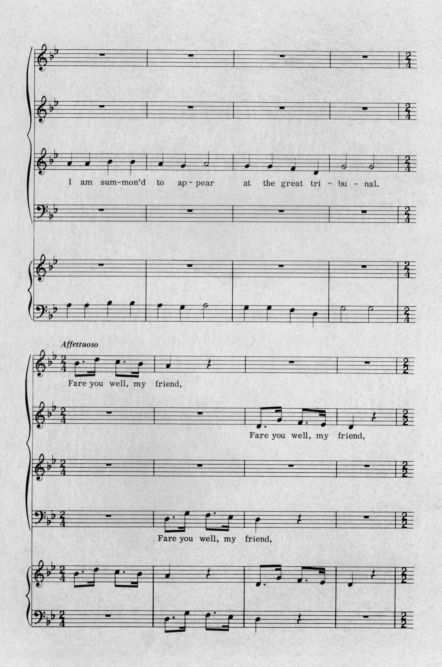

I am sum-mon'd to ap-pear at the great tri - bu - nal.

Affettuoso

Fare you well, my friend,

Fare you well, my friend,

Fare you well, my friend,

156

And God grant we may_ meet

And God grant we may meet

Languishing

Fare you well, my friend, And God grant we may meet

And God grant we may meet

in that land of Har - mo - ny, where the wick - ed_

in that_land of_ Har - mo - ny, where the_wick - ed

in that land of Har - mo - ny, where the wick - ed

in that land of Har - mo - ny, where the wick - ed

158

1794

THE STRAW BONNET

The American market was well provided with solo songs in the last two decades of the eighteenth century. Most of them, however, were imported from England in print or printed in this country with the notice that they had been "received with acclaim" at Vauxhall Gardens, a favorite outdoor place of entertainment in London, or as part of one of the many stage productions that London enjoyed. Songs composed in this country were rare and, except for the earlier efforts of Francis Hopkinson, were generally by musicians who had been born or trained abroad.

Mary Ann Pownall must have been an especially interesting person to come on the American scene. She brought with her the glamor of English success, for she was well known in the theater and at Vauxhall, and she quickly became a principal artist with the Old American Company in Boston. She is apparently the first woman composer in this country to have her works appear in print. She joined with James Hewitt in the publication of their *Six Songs for the Harpsichord or Piano Forte,* and she composed both words and music for one of those songs. The poet of *The Straw Bonnet,* however, is not identified. The song is strongly reminiscent of English theater music of its decade: the poem reflects an upper-class view of the rustic life; the music is more sophisticated than most of the native American pieces with its graces, a miniature cadenza, and the affected "Scotch snap" rhythm in its concluding phrase. The abbreviation "Sy," at the end of the text section, appears in much music of this period, indicating a "Symphony"; that is, an instrumental conclusion.

Mrs. (Mary) Pownall and J. Hewitt, *Six Songs for the Harpsichord or Piano Forte* (New York: For the Authors, 1794).

The Straw Bonnet

Allegretto

Mrs. [Mary] Pownall (1794)

Pia.

for.

When fa[i] - ries are light - ed by night's Sil - ver
I saw the straw Bon - net he bought at the

Queen and feast it in Mead - ow or
Fair with Rose col - our'd Rib - bons, to

dance on the Green my Swain leaves his
deck Sal - ly's Hair The shoe ties of

Pat – ty   and   Ruth   he for – sook   and de –
to part,   yet   I know   when I   see   him a –

ceiv'd   yet his words   are so   sweet   and like
gain   That his words   and his   looks   will like

Truth   so ap – pear   that I   par – don the
Truth   so ap – pear   I shall   par – don the

Trea – son   the Trai – tor   so   dear.   *for.*   Sy.

162

1794

MAJOR ANDRE'S COMPLAINT

Two centuries ago, a spy who lost his life in the service of his country was, to his own people at least, a romantic hero. Nathan Hale has come into our history in that light, but his plight was not commemorated in song. The British spy, John André, caught the American fancy both during and after his life. He was known to his friends in this country as a charming young officer of artistic sensibilities. Upon his first capture, he was exchanged and reassigned to duty. Subsequently, he negotiated with Benedict Arnold for the betrayal of West Point, was captured, tried, and hanged at Washington's headquarters.

The earliest printed version of *Major Andre's Complaint* is the one printed here. Benjamin Carr, an English composer, had opened the first music store in this country shortly after his arrival in 1793. This must have been one of his first publications. It remained current until at least 1804, when it was again popular as one of the songs in the musical show *The Nightingale.* Its appeal at that late date can not have been due to the lingering memories of Tories from a generation before.

Major Andre's Complaint (Philadelphia: Carr & Co's. Musical Repository. [1794]).

163

MAJOR ANDRE'S COMPLAINT

Price 12 Cents

Philadelphia Printed at Carr & Co? Mufical Repofitory

Return en_rap_turd hours when De_lia's heart was mine when

fhe with wreaths of flow'rs my temples did en_twine no

jea_lou_fy nor care cor_ro_ded in my breaft nor

vifions light as air _ pre_fi_ _ded o'er my reft.

2	3
Since I'm remov'd from ftate	Now nightly round my bed
And hid adien to time	No airy vifion's play
At my unhappy fate	Nor flowrets deck my head
Let Delia not repine	Each vernal holliday
But may the mighty Jove	But far from thefe fad plains
Her crown with happinefs	The lovely Delia flies
This grant ye pow'rs above	While rack'd with jealous pains
And take my foul to blifs.	Her wretched ANDRE dies.

164

A sketch of Major John André, made by himself the day before he was hanged as a spy at Washington's headquarters in 1780. (Culver Pictures).

The Favorite BALLAD of THE

Poor Black Boy

In the new Musical Farce of The PRIZE

Composed by Storace

—— Price 20 Cents ——

Philadelphia Printed at Carr & Co's Musical Repository

1794

POOR
BLACK BOY

Eileen Southern wrote, in *The Music of Black Americans* (New York: W. W. Norton & Co., 1971), that "so-called 'Negro songs' had been in circulation in England as early as the mid-eighteenth century; they were performed on the concert stage and published in song collections." She and other writers have noted that such songs and some dances appeared sporadically in this country before the end of the century. Generally these were published, when they appeared in print at all, in collections containing other music. *Poor Black Boy* fits that pattern. It was composed by Stephen Storace, an English composer of operas and theatrical music, and it was introduced into this country not as an example of indigenous music, but as a popular tune from a London stage show. It appeared as part of a collection, but the edition reproduced here was printed and sold as a separate song.

The combination of this crude attempt at dialect and the stylized music of the London stage may not have seemed strange to English audiences, for they were not in any way in touch with America's slave population. The piece had no direct influence on later minstrel songs, and it stands here simply as another example of imported music that was reprinted in this country.

Stephen Storace, *Poor Black Boy* (Philadelphia: Carr & Co., 1794).

no   and where away   my   Mafsa   go   go poor Black Boy"   go

"poor Black   Boy"   and where away   my Mafsa go   go "poor Black   Boy."

2

You good to me dat keepy here
No Mafsa dat you never fear
Long time deftroy
Me know death kill but leave one part
He never kill de loving heart
Of "Poor Black Boy."

3

Me figh with you when you be fad
And when you merry much and glad
Me fha're your joy
For do my face be darky hue
Theres ftill a faithful foul and true
In "Poor Black Boy."

Flute or Guittar

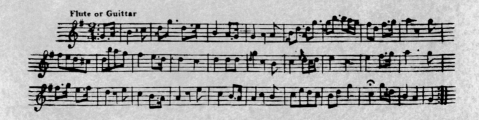

This watercolor was probably painted on a plantation between Charleston and Orangeburg, South Carolina. The musical instruments are of Yoruban origin, and the dance itself is probably also Yoruban. *"The Old Plantation."* Artist unknown. Late eighteenth century. (Abby Aldrich Rockefeller Folk Art Collection).

The Volunteers

Susannah Rowson

Alexander Reinagle (1795)

1795

FINALE from THE VOLUNTEERS

All that survives of *The Volunteers* is the text and music to the songs. Any dialogue that held the piece together cannot be found, so there is no clear idea of its plot. Susannah Haswell Rowson, the librettist, was a poet of some distinction, although these texts do not show it. Alexander Reinagle, whose *Federal March* (page 95) was well known and who was competent in the idiom of the Classical period, should also not be judged only by this fragment.

The finale, printed here, does not illuminate the cast of characters because only three of them are on stage. From the entire composition, we can determine more about them. Aura, who sings first, is an unclaimed treasure of uncertain age; Jemima is a farmer's wife, happy with her lot; Omeeah is an older woman whose position in the plot remains unclear. The men of whom they sing are: Thomas, Jemima's husband; Millikin, a gay young blade; Trueman, our hero in uniform; Jerry, a cynic about women; and Manly, a seaman. Their purpose in going off to war is not clear, although there is a statement that they will "follow Wayne." The assignments of Anthony Wayne were too numerous and widespread for any plot connection to be discerned. Whatever the humor of this farce was, it existed in the dialogue, a situation that demonstrates again how music serves only as an adjunct to the plot when a popular audience is the target.

Alexander Reinagle, *The Volunteers* (Philadelphia, 1795).

with the vine and bid the he - ro's wel - come home.

Jemima

By them pro - tect - ed from a - larms, For them our dai - ly

prayers___ shall___ rise; still may suc - cess at - tend their arms, and

Omeeah

shame pur - sue their En - e - mies. And when the war - riors

172

A New Assistant for the Piano Forte

Tempo di Gavotta

Francis Linley (1796)

Tempo di Minuetto

174

1796
A NEW ASSISTANT FOR THE PIANO-FORTE

The composer of the first piano instruction book printed in America was Francis Linley, a blind English organist. The year 1796 was of great importance in his life, for it was then that he bought a thriving music business in London, the business failed, his wife (also blind) left him, he came to America, and his *New Assistant* was published in Baltimore. He returned to England in 1799.

The volume consists of a few pages of basic instruction; the staff, clefs, note names, and a short dictionary. Obviously it is intended for people with no musical experience. The speed with which the lessons progress is too great for such students, as is clear from the two samples given here. The first is the initial lesson. The two hands are expected to play together from the outset, and the only help given is the fingerings for all the notes. The plus sign is used to indicate the thumb, and the other fingers are numbered consecutively, the index finger being designated number 1. The first of six sonatas appears five pages later, and its complexity shows the skills that should have been acquired within such a short time. Fingerings were printed throughout the sonata, but they are omitted here. The fourth sonata is for two performers. There are no dynamic marks, but musical terms and notational accuracy through the volume are clear and consistent with a high level of European training. The terms *Gavotta* and *Minuetto* that appear in the examples printed here do not appear in the short dictionary. Unless the student knew the terms from elsewhere, they would have been meaningless to him.

Francis Linley, *A New Assistant for the Piano-Forte* (Baltimore: L. Carr, 1796).

175

Money Musk

[Flute or Violin]

Martini's march in Henry IV

[Flute or Violin I]

[Flute or Violin II]

TWO
PIECES
from EVENING
AMUSEMENT

Music for amateurs, to be played in private gatherings among friends, serves as a gauge of the musical sophistication of a generation. Collections such as *Evening Amusement* were published in Europe, to be sure, but they were by far outnumbered by full-scale sonatas, sets of variations, and *divertimenti* by composers of small and great reputation. These more substantial (and often tedious) works did not make their way into America, and we may assume that amateur taste and skill are represented by the examples shown here.

The music is advertised as being "for 1 and 2 German Flutes or Violins," a situation no doubt dictated by the need to sell as many copies as possible. Still, the music appears to have been arranged for the convenience of the violinist, for there are notes below the range of the flute and several instances occur when double-stops, unplayable on a wind instrument, are written, as at the cadence points in the march.

Money musk is a fiddle tune of unknown age, and it is still played by country fiddlers. *Martini's march* is not by the famous Italian G. B. Martini (Padre Martini), but rather by Johann Paul Aegidius Schwartendorf, who adopted the name Martini il Tedesco, and whose opera *Henri IV* was first performed November 14, 1774, in Paris. It is more likely that it was included here because of its appeal to amateurs rather than because of the fame of its composer.

Evening Amusement containing Fifty Airs, Songs, . . . Marches and Minuets (Philadelphia: B. Carr, [1796]).

181

178?

THE ANACREONTIC SONG

and ADAMS AND LIBERTY 1798

The sanctity of our national anthem, and the propriety of its use and rendition, have been the concern of musicians, legislators, and the public for some time. The stages through which the music has passed, and the various words that have been written to the tune are the subject of an extensive monograph and some short studies. It will serve well enough to demonstrate eighteenth-century use by comparing the two versions given here, since the marriage of *The Anacreontic Song* melody with the words we now use did not take place until 1814.

The Anacreontic Society in London, a club of musical amateurs during the last third of the century, had as its song the first piece printed here. It was a musical toast to Anacreon, with references to wine and love, the former of which was actively pursued at the meetings. The melody became extremely popular in this country, and it served as the vehicle for numerous sets of words, many of them patriotic or nationalistic because of its vigorous character. Much of the original vigor was lost when the rousing duple-meter setting of *The Anacreontic Song* was

Chorus.

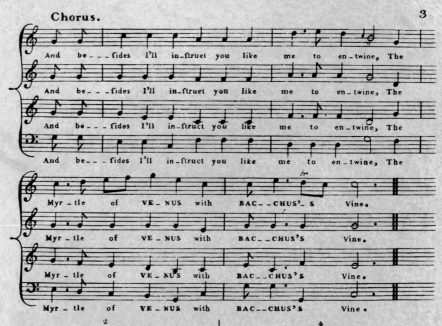

And be___sides I'll in_struct you like me to en_twine, The Myr_tle of VE_NUS with BAC__CHUS'S Vine.

2

The news through OLYMPUS immediately flew;
When OLD THUNDER pretended to give himself Airs—
If these Mortals are suffer'd their Scheme to pursue,
The Devil a Goddess will stay above Stairs.
"Hark! already they cry,
"In Transports of Joy
"Away to the Sons of ANACREON we'll fly,
"And there, with good Fellows, we'll learn to intwine
"The Myrtle of VENUS with BACCHUS'S Vine.

3

"The YELLOW-HAIR'D GOD and his nine fusty Maids,
"From HELICON'S Banks will incontinent flee
"IDALIA will boast but of tenantless Shades,
"And the bi-forked Hill a mere Desart will be
"My Thunder no fear on't,
"Shall soon do its Errand,
"And, dam'me! I'll swinge the Ringleaders I warrant,
"I'll trim the young Dogs, for thus daring to twine
The Myrtle of VENUS with BACCHUS'S Vine.

4

APOLLO rose up; and said, "Pr'ythee ne'er quarrel,
"Good King of the Gods with my Vot'ries below:
"Your Thunder is useless—then, shewing his Laurel,
Cry'd. "Sic evitabile fulmen, you know!
"Then over each Head
"My Laurels I'll spread
"So my Sons from your Crackers no Mischief shall dread,
"Whilst snug in their Club-Room, they Jovially twine
"The Myrtle of VENUS with BACCHUS'S Vine.

5

Next MOMUS got up with his risible Phiz,
And swore with APOLLO he'd chearfull join—
"The full Tide of Harmony still shall be his,
"But the Song, and the Catch & the Laugh shall be mine
"Then, JOVE, be not jealous
"Of these honest Fellows,
Cry'd JOVE, "We relent, since the Truth you now tell us;
"And swear, by OLD STYX, that they long shall intwine
The Myrtle of VENUS with BACCHUS'S Vine.

6

Ye Sons of ANACREON, then join Hand in Hand;
Preserve Unanimity, Friendship, and Love!
'Tis your's to support what's so happily plann'd;
You've the Sanction of Gods, and the FIAT of JOVE.
While thus we agree,
Our Toast let it be.
May our Club flourish happy, united, and free!
And long may the Sons of ANACREON intwine
The Myrtle of VENUS with BACCHUS'S Vine

For the Guitar

To ANACREON in Heav'n, where he fat in full Glee, a few Sons of Harmo ny

fent a Pe ti tion, that he their In fpir er and Patron would be; when this

Anfwer ar riv'd from the jol ly OLD GRECIAN "Voice, Fiddle, and Flute, no

longer be mute; I'll lend you my name, and in fpire you to boot; and be

fides, I'll inftruct you like me to in twine the Myrtle of VENUS with

Chorus

BAC CHUS'S Vine, and be fides, I'll inftruct you like me to intwine, the

Myrtle of VENUS with BAC CHUS'S Vine.

For the German Flute

To A NACREON, in Heav'n, where he fat in full Glee, a few Sons of Harmony

fent a Pe ti tion, that he their In fpir er and Patron would be; when this

Anfwer arriv'd from the jolly OLD GRECIAN Voice, Fiddle, and Flute, no

longer be mute, I'll lend you my name and in fpire you to boot; and be

fides, I'll inftruct you like me to in twine the Myrtle of VENUS with

Chorus

BAC CHUS'S Vine, and be fides, I'll inftruct you like me to intwine the

Myrtle of VENUS with BACCHUS'S Vine.

185

Adams and Liberty

Thomas Paine (Robert Treat Paine)

Tune: The Anacreontic Song

Allegretto

1. Ye sons of Co - lum - bia, who brave - ly have fought, For those
8. Should the Tem - pest of War o - ver - shad - ow our land, Its
9. Let Fame to the world sound A - mer - i - ca's voice; No In -

rights, which un - stain'd from your Sires had de - scend - ed, May you
bolts could ne'er rend Free - dom's tem - ple a - sun - der; For, un -
trigues can her sons from their Gov - ern - ment sev - er; Her

long taste the bless - ings your val - our has bought, And your
moved, at its por - tal, would Wash - ing - ton stand, And re -
Pride is her Ad - ams— his Laws are her choice, And shall

converted to triple meter as it was used in *Adams and Liberty*. The walking bass of the closing section may have been an early attempt to restore sturdiness to the piece.

A certain confusion exists over the identity of the Thomas Paine, M.A., who is listed as the author of the words to *Adams and Liberty*. He was not the English-born patriot-writer, but rather a son of Robert Treat Paine, a signer of the Declaration of Independence. First named Thomas, he was renamed Robert Treat after the death of a brother so named. A renegade intellectual who defied authority and society, he was nevertheless a good poet. The text of *Adams and Liberty* was written for the Massachusetts Charitable Fire Society in 1798. There are nine stanzas, each of which lauds an ideal or an individual connected with the new nation. It is alleged that the stanza about Washington was not part of the original poem, but that it was written at the specific demand of a host who withheld a glass of wine from Paine until the stanza should be penned. It was written on the spot, and it is judged by many to be the best of the entire poem.

The Anacreontic Song (London: Longman & Broderip, [178-]).

Adams and Liberty: The Boston Patriotic Song (Boston: Thomas and Andrews, 1798).

sons reap the soil, which your fa - thers de - fend - ed. 'Mid the
pulse, with his Breast, the as - saults of the Thun - der! His
flour - ish, till Lib - er - ty slum - ber for - ev - er! Then u -

reign of mild peace, May your na - tion in - crease With the
sword, from the sleep Of its scab - bard, would leap, And con -
nite, heart and hand, Like Leo - ni - das' band, And

glo - ry of Rome, and the wis - dom of Greece;
duct, with its point, ev - ery flash to the deep.
swear to the God of the o - cean and land,

And ne'er may the sons of Co - lum - bia be slaves, While the
For ne'er shall the sons of Co - lum - bia be slaves, While the
That ne'er shall the sons of Co - lum - bia be slaves, While the

earth bears a plant, or the sea rolls its waves.

188

1798 ?

WASHINGTON AND INDEPENDENCE

Patriotism was a noble word to Americans at the century's close. It rang with conviction in conversations, speeches, printed documents, and musical compositions. Often coupled with the ideals of liberty, independence, and commercial development, those utterances stirred the American people to a chauvinism that was intensified by their sudden liberation from foreign domination. When the heroic names of Adams and Washington were added, the cup of national pride filled to the brim.

The high regard in which George Washington was held has not been accorded any later person. Lincoln's presidency and death made their impacts upon a nation divided, and subsequent heroes have been too much identified with party or turmoil to be given the adulation to which Washington fell heir. Marches and songs bore his name in their titles; his picture adorned the covers of still others; pieces were dedicated to his honor; and, upon his death, the general outpouring of national grief naturally found its way into music.

Victor Pelissier was well-known in New York as a horn virtuoso and composer. He wrote operas, incidental music to a number of plays, and some short pieces. *Washington and Independence* shares with much patriotic music of that time a strongly martial character. Rousing tunes were not only suitable to the topic, but they could be identified more easily than the lyric material that was a model of bland conformity.

Victor Pelissier, *Washington and Independence: A Favorite Patriotic Song* (New York: G. Gilfert, [1798?]).

189

Washington and Independence

Victor Pelissier (1798?)

1. When Free-dom's sons in these blest Climes, A Ref - uge Sought from
2. But Soon the Sound of war Be - gan, The sav - age and the
3. At length by Brit - ain's wrong Im - pell'd, They tore in twain all
4. Then Wash - ing - ton, O! Glo - rious name! 'Mid He - roes and bold

Eng - land's Woes, They bade a - dieu to Eu - rop's Crimes, And
Gaul, by turns, In - flict the wound On Suf - fering man; And
ear - ly ties, With arm of steel their rights up - held, And
states-men shone, Se - cure - ly built his coun - try's fame, And

Hail'd the Em - pire as it rose.
peace re - tires while ven - geance burns.
self - sup - port - ed see them rise.
more se - cure - ly fix'd his own.

The Federal Constitution and Liberty Forever

adapted by J. Hewitt (1798)

1. Po - ets may sing of their He - li - con streams Their
2. Ad - ams, the man of our choice, guides the helm, No
3. free Na - vi - ga - tion, Com - merce and Trade, We'll
4. Trum - pet shall swell in Wash - ing - ton's praise, And

Gods___ and their He - roes are fab - u - lous dreams their
tem - pest can harm us, no storm___ o - ver - whelm, No
seek___ for no foe of no foe___ be a - fraid, We'll
time___ grant a fur - lough to length - en his days, And

Gods___ and their He - roes are fab - u - lous dreams They
tem - pest can harm___ us, no storm___ o - ver - whelm, Our
seek___ for no foe___ of no foe___ be a - fraid. Our
time___ grant a fur - lough to length - en his days, May

193

To many Americans, Washington had become their invincible leader, a symbol of the new nation's hopes for greatness. John Trumbull's *Capture of the Hessians at Trenton* shows him as the generous victor, extending his hand to the dying Colonel Rall. (Yale University Art Gallery).

194

THE
FEDERAL
CONSTITUTION
AND LIBERTY
FOREVER

The passage of years often casts a rosy haze over the realities of the creative process. Subjects and emphases of art works may well be consistent with the convictions of their creators, but the subject may also be chosen with an eye to its commercial appeal as well as its ethical basis. So it must have become with our ancestors. The poets, composers, and performers of music at the century's close were often people who earned their livelihood in their art, not toying with it after the manner of a Francis Hopkinson.

ne'er sang a line half so grand___ so di - vine As the
sheet an-chor's sure And our bark___ rides se - cure, So___
frig - ates shall ride Our de - fence___ and our pride; Our___
health save the thread Of de - light___ round his head; No___

glo - ri - ous toast we Co - lum - bians boast The
here's to the toast we Co - lum - bians boast The
Tars guard our coast and huz - za___ to our toast The
na - tion can boast Such a name___ such a toast The

Fed - eral Con - sti - tu - tion boys and Lib - er - ty for
Fed - eral Con - sti - tu - tion and the Pres - i - dent for
Fed - eral Con - sti - tu - tion, Trade and Com - merce boys for
Fed - eral Con - sti - tu - tion boys and Wash - ing - ton for

ev - er the Fed - eral Con - sti - tu - tion boys and
ev - er the Fed - eral Con - sti - tu - tion and the
ev - er the Fed - eral Con - sti - tu - tion, Trade and
ev - er the Fed - eral Con - sti - tu - tion boys and

Lib - er - ty for ev - er.
Pres - i - dent for ev - er.
Com - merce boys for ev - er.
Wash - ing - ton for ev - er.

James Hewitt was one of the new professionals who settled in our principal cities in the 1790s. He came to New York an experienced orchestra player, quickly established himself in the concert life of that city, and became known as a composer and publisher as well. His operas and his instrumental music capitalized on America's patriotic fervor and sense of emerging history. In this song he combined one of several pieces named *Washington's March* (composer unknown) and *Yankee Doodle*. This arrangement may be one of the first pieces issued by his publishing house, for it was in 1798 that he bought the New York branch of Carr's Musical Repository and made it the foundation of his own business.

William Milns, who wrote the words, was apparently known to New York audiences from a number of stage works to which he had written songs.

James Hewitt, arr., *The Federal Constitution and Liberty Forever* (New York: J. Hewitt's Musical Repository, 1798).

The Battle of Trenton

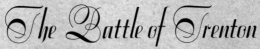

INTRODUCTION
Slow

James Hewitt (1798)

1798

THE
BATTLE OF
TRENTON

The Battle of Trenton, December 26, 1776, was one of the early decisive American victories. Washington's forces crossed the Delaware, surprised the Hessians who were less than alert after their Christmas celebrations, and proved that Americans were able to win at hand-to-hand combat with bayonets.

The version of that assault by the Hessian Adjutant General Major Baurmeister (in *Revolution in America*, trans. by Gernhard A. Uhlendorf, Rutgers University Press, 1957), reads:

An hour after sunrise, Lossberg's, Knyphausen's, and Rall's Regiments were surprised in Trenton by more than ten thousand rebels. They were badly treated and made prisoners, losing their guns, colors, and all equipage. The post at headquarters, consisting of one hundred men of Rall's brigade, Lieutenant von Grothausen, and the English dragoons, and as many as three hundred men of the three battalions, escaped to Colonel von Donop. Moreover, seventy-five picked men under Lieutenant von Winzingerode of Lossberg's Regiment are stationed here, and an even greater number are in the hospitals. Many officers escaped and are sick, but many others died with Colonel Rall.

The painting, *Battle of Trenton,* after E. L. Henry, shows Washington leading his forces in that attack.

Franz Kotzwara's *Battle of Prague* had been such a success that it spawned a number of imitations. In 1792 François Devienne marked another military victory with his orchestral composition, *La Bataille de Gemmapp*, giving musical rebirth to one of the early battles of the French Revolutionary Wars. In that year the French had defeated the Austrians at the little town of Jemmapes, near Mons in Belgium. Devienne's composition for twenty instruments appeared shortly thereafter and, by 1796, was printed as a piano solo by the New York publisher G. Gilfert. It ran through the same series of pictorial sections as had Kotzwara's piece, complete with cannon shots, trumpet calls, patriotic tunes, advances and retreats of armies, and the cries of the wounded. Devienne possessed enough skill as a composer that his piece was less wearying than others of that genre, but compositions of that nature seldom contained much that was not stylized and obvious.

Whether it was one or both of these pieces that influenced James Hewitt to compose *The Battle of Trenton*, the pattern was clear. Hewitt crammed more material into the first page of his piece than had his predecessors. It contained a Slow Introduction, Army in Motion, General Orders, Acclamation of Americans, Drum Beats to Arms, and the opening measures of *Washington's March.*

Hewitt's piece moved more slowly after the opening page, and the obligatory sections involving the shooting, the flight of the enemy (Hessians in this case), the minor-mode grief for comrades killed in battle, and the closing section of general rejoicing all appear in more leisurely fashion. Slightly more than half of the piece is given here, 249 measures being omitted. Not much is lost by these deletions, for the 135 measures that conclude the composition are hardly more inventive than the rest of the "general rejoicing" section. The only new device there is the use of contrasting loud and soft passages.

Kotzwara quoted *God Save the King* in his battle piece, obviously courting the English market; Devienne quoted *La Marseioise* and the French revolutionary song *Ça Ira*; Hewitt inserted his own modified version of *Yankee Doodle*, the tune being at a high point of popularity by that time.

The world was to be given much more battle music in the coming years, some of it from Europe, some from America, but almost all of it inferior to the other descriptive concert music that was written.

James Hewitt, *The Battle of Trenton* (New York: For the Author, 1798).

200

201

General Orders

Acclamation of the Americans

203

206

Defeat of the Hessians

Flight of the Hessians

65 measures omitted

Andantino semplice The Hessians surrender themselves Prisoners of War

208

Articles of Capitulation signed

f

Fine

D.S.

Grief of the Americans for the loss of their Comrades killed in the Engagement
Lento con Expressione [sic]

211

212

213

* ♩ in original

214

216

The final 135 measures are omitted.

A Funeral Elegy

Abraham Wood (1800)

1800

A FUNERAL ELEGY

George Washington died on December 14th, 1799, and was buried at Mount Vernon on December 18th. Congress did not receive word of his death until the day of the funeral, and the information reached the rest of the country even more slowly. Memorial services, civic observances, orations, musical compositions, and eulogies of various kinds became almost commonplace. Between December 26th and the following February 22nd, at least 300 eulogies were given in 185 towns. The music that accompanies much of this deeply felt national grief was a varied lot, ranging from simple songs and funeral marches to works of cantata length. No small amount of music can be selected as typical of these pieces. This section of choral music and a solo song from a set of pieces (page 227) will supply at least some of the variety of this music.

Abraham Wood was a self-taught composer who earned his livelihood as a dresser of cloth. He had been a drummer in the Revolutionary War, but his musical skills were not equal to the development of ideas in extended pieces where repetitions of text were necessary. Still, his honest attempt to express the grief that overwhelmed the country is worth our examination here. The composition continues for several pages beyond this section. The occasion on which it was performed is not known.

Abraham Wood, *A Funeral Elegy on the Death of General George Washington* (Boston: Thomas & Andrews, 1800).

221

Wash-ing - ton! the scourge of Ty-rants_ past, And awe of Prin-ces

Wash-ing - ton! the scourge of Ty-rants_ past, And awe of Prin-ces

Wash-ing - ton! the scourge of Ty-rants_ past, And awe of Prin-ces

Wash-ing - ton! the scourge of Ty-rants_ past, And awe of Prin-ces

yet un - born. Glo - ry with all her lamps shall

yet un - born. Glo - ry with all her lamps shall

yet un - born. Glo - ry with all her lamps shall

burn, And watch the War-rior's sleep - ing clay, 'Till the last

burn, And watch the War-rior's sleep - ing clay, 'Till the last

burn, And watch the War-rior's sleep - ing clay, 'Till the last

burn, And watch the War-rior's sleep - ing clay, 'Till the last

trum-pet rouse his urn, To aid the tri - umphs of the

trum-pet rouse his urn, To aid the tri - umphs of the

trum-pet rouse his urn, To aid the tri - umphs of the

225

1800

MOUNT VERNON

The opening words of the eulogy on Washington delivered by Congressman Henry Lee of Virginia at the German Lutheran Church in Philadelphia on December 26, 1799, have been memorized by almost every American school-child, but few people know those words in context. The depth of feeling that was expressed for America's hero— a reverence that appears to have been common to all walks of life—is better seen in a larger extract from that oration.

First in war, first in peace and first in the hearts of his countrymen, he was second to none in the humble and endearing scenes of private life. Pious, just, humane, temperate and sincere—uniform, dignified and commanding—his example was as edifying to all around him as were the effects of that lasting example.... Correct throughout, vice shuddered in his presence and virtue always felt his fostering hand. The purity of his private character gave effulgence to his public virtues. ... Such was the man for whom our nation mourns.

The music that was performed at that memorial service was elaborate, employing singers and instrumentalists who relied strongly on music by Handel.

For a commemorative service two months later, the music was composed by an American. The lapse of time permitted the composition, copying, and rehearsal of the several pieces, and Oliver Holden, one of the leading church musicians of the day, produced a service consisting of nine sections, the third of which is printed here. It is the only solo piece in the set.

Mount Vernon

Oliver Holden (1800)

From Vern-on's Mount, be-hold the He-ro___ rise, Re-

splend - ent___forms at - tend him through the skies; The shades of war-worn

Vet - 'rans round him throng, And lead___ en - wrapt their hon - or'd

Chief a-long A lau-rel wreath th'im-mor-tal War-ren bears; An

arch tri-umph - al Mer-cer's hand pre-pares; Young Law-rence 'erst th'a-

228

veng - ing bolt of war, With pert__ ma - jes - tic guides the glitt - 'ring

car: Mont - gom - ery's god - like form di - rects the

way, And Greene un - folds the__ gates of end - less__ day.

While an - gels__ trum - pet - tongu'd pro - claim through air.__ Due hon - ors, due

hon - ors, due__ hon - ors for the First Of Men pre - pare.

I. Funeral Anthem—The Sound of the Harp ceaseth
II. Columbia's Guardian Sleeps in Dust!
III. Mount Vernon. A Solo
IV. A Dirge—Peace to his Soul, the fatal Hour is past!
V. A Hymn—And is th'ILLUSTRIOUS CHIEFTAIN dead?
VI. Anniversary Dirge—Is this the Anniversary so dear?
VII. Masonic Dirge—While every Bard and Orator displays
VIII. Funeral Hymn—Up to thy Throne, Eternal King
IX. An Ode—Now let your plaintive Numbers gently rise

The music was presented, along with a discourse and prayers, at Boston's Brattle Street Church on February 22, 1800. After such solemn observances on the anniversary of his birth, Washington's nation returned to its normal business.

Oliver Holden, *Sacred Dirges, Hymns, and Anthems,* COMMEMORATIVE OF THE DEATH OF GENERAL GEORGE WASHINGTON, THE GUARDIAN OF HIS COUNTRY, AND THE FRIEND OF MAN (Boston: I. Thomas and E. T. Andrews, {1800}).

1800

HANDEL'S WATER PIECE

Learning to play a musical instrument in America at the turn of the nineteenth century was a more difficult process than it was abroad. Conservatories, private teachers, and a host of professional musicians who did some teaching were common sources of study for the hopeful musician in Germany, France, England, and other countries, the affluent paying for study in cash, the less fortunate hoping to win scholarships or apprenticeships. In America, on the other hand, the best musicians (rarely the peers of the foreign masters, although capable) were clustered in a few cities, and the thought of entering a profession that supported so few in the good life was less attractive to young Americans than the prospect of entering business or learning a trade.

Nevertheless, the prospect of attaining some skill in music was part of the American dream. It was not necessary to learn music to equal the skills of Thomas Jefferson, Francis Hopkinson, or Benjamin Franklin. Music was a social grace among the wealthy, but it was no less an ornament to the lives of the multitude. There was a place for music in this country, but it was not yet one that would being fortune and social recognition. Most of the interest among those who could not obtain private instruction was in some manner or other of self instructor, a book that could show how to do it, even though it might not show how to do it well. There was a considerable interest in music and instruments as the country grew, but it may be symptomatic that one astute immigrant,

Handel's Water Piece

from *The Instrumental Assistant*
compiled by Samuel Holyoke (1800)

233

John Jacob Astor, sold his instrument and music store in New York, turning to more profitable business in furs and real estate.

Samuel Holyoke, a Harvard graduate, saw a place in this framework for an instructional volume that would provide pieces for the performers to play together. He hoped to eradicate the fuging style from vocal music, and he appeared to be interested in promoting a higher level of instrumental skill. *The Instrumental Assistant* began to appear in 1800, and it continued to be published until 1807. The first volume contained eight lessons, including fingering charts and instructions on producing a good tone, for the various instruments. The lessons were followed by pieces for the students to play together. The sixty-second piece in the volume is printed here. It is not odd that a piece by Handel should be published in this country, for Handel's fame in England had spread across the Atlantic. What is strange is that this section of the famous *Water Music* should be one of the variant versions of the Overture to the second Suite in D, and not the best known version.

Samuel Holyoke, *The Instrumental Assistant. Containing Instructions for the Violin, German-Flute, Clarionett, Bass-Viol, and Hautboy* . . . Vol. I. (Exeter, N.H.: H. Ranlet, 1800).

LITTLE
BOY BLEW
and
SHAKESPEARE'S
WILLOW

Benjamin Carr advertised the publication and sale of a journal for the pianoforte, but he supplied an equal amount of vocal music under the same title. In his first issue, he wrote:

The Musical Journal is published in two Sections viz: One of Vocal Music every 1st and 3d Monday & one of Instrumental Music every 2d and 4th Monday of each Month throughout the year.... Selected and Arranged by Benjamin Carr. Who from extensive materials in his possession, a regular supply of new Music from Europe and the assistance of Men of Genius in this Country hopes he shall present the Public with a work that for novelty and cheapness will be fully worthy their patronage.

Carr certainly influenced the spread of European works and Continental taste. He published works by Haydn, Viotti, Boccherini, Pleyel, Reichardt, and the Englishmen Hook and Atwood. Music of that level could be heard by concertgoers in the principal cities. Carr's publications

Little Boy Blew

Benjamin Carr (1800)

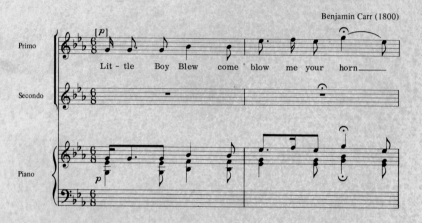

Primo

Lit - tle Boy Blew come blow me your horn——

Secondo

Piano

Lit - tle Boy Blew come blow me your horn—— come

Lit - tle Boy Blew come blow me your horn—— come

*If a lady sings the Second the lower are to be sung.

236

Where is the lit-tle boy that looks af-ter__ the__ sheep

un-der the hay-stack fast__ a-sleep

fast_____ a-

sleep   fast_____ a - sleep

[pp]

[pp]

fast_____ a - sleep

pp

238

made study and performance of it available not only to urbanites, but also to interested amateurs in places less convenient to the concert halls.

The contribution of this one man to vocal music was significant, not only in the volume of imported and domestic pieces he published, but also in his own composition where he brought a new dimension to texts and accompaniments. The usual keyboard accompaniment for songs had consisted of simple left-hand parts, one bass note at a time against the melody. In his *Little Boy Blew*, described in his *Journal* as a "Nursery Song for two Voices," Carr wrote a fully harmonic keyboard part that employed shifting registers along with the complete chords, but was still tied to the old system of duplicating the principal melody in the right hand. His *Willow* song brought the illusion of Shakespearean text to American musical settings, quite a contrast to the poetic content of earlier American songs. Still, it was not Shakespeare's words that were set to music, but Carr's modification of them. The text from *Othello*, given below, should be compared with Carr's version.

> The poor soul sat sighing by a sycamore tree,
> Sing all a green willow;
> Her hand on her bosom, her head on her knee,
> Sing willow, willow, willow:
> The fresh streams ran by her, and murmur'd her moans;
> Sing willow, willow, willow:
> Her salt tears fell from her, and soften'd the stones;—
> Sing willow, willow, willow:
> Sing all a green willow must be my garland.

Benjamin Carr, *The Musical Journal for the Piano Forte* (Baltimore, 1800).

Shakespeares Willow

Slow and Plaintive

Benjamin Carr (1800)

1. A poor soul sat sigh-ing un-der a syc-a-more tree O Wil-low Wil-low Wil-low with her hand on her bos-om her head on her knee O O
2. She sigh'd in her sing-ing sigh'd and af-ter each moan O Wil-low Wil-low Wil-low I am dead to all pleas-ure my true love is gone O O
3. The wil-low now bids me bids me de-spair and to die — O Wil-low Wil-low Wil-low So hang it friends o'er me in grave where I lie O O

Wil-low Wil-low Wil-low Wil-low sing O the green Wil-low O the green Wil-low O the green Wil-low shall be my gar-land.